Edexcel
GCSE MODULAR MATHE
Examples and Practic

CW00859901

INTERMEDIATE

Stage 1

Karen Hughes   Trevor Johnson   Peter Jolly
David Kent   Keith Pledger

Endorsed by **edexcel**

heinemann.co.uk
✓ Free online support
✓ Useful weblinks
✓ 24 hour online ordering

01865 888058

Heinemann
Inspiring generations

About this book

This *Examples and Practice* book is designed to help you get the best possible grade in your Edexcel GCSE maths examination. The authors are senior examiners and coursework moderators and have a good understanding of Edexcel's requirements.

Intermediate Stage 1 Examples and Practice covers all the topics that will be tested in your Intermediate Stage 1 examination. You can use this book to revise in the run up to your exam, or you can use it throughout the course, alongside the *Edexcel GCSE Maths* Intermediate core textbook.

References in the contents list for each section of the book tell you where to find the most relevant paragraph of the specification. For example, NA2a refers to Number and Algebra, paragraph 2, section a.

Helping you prepare for your exam

To help you prepare, each topic offers:
- **Key points** to reinforce the key teaching concepts
- **Teaching references** showing you where the relevant material is covered in both the old and new editions of the *Edexcel GCSE Maths* Intermediate core textbook. These references show you where to find full explanations of concepts, and additional worked examples e.g.

> Teaching reference:
> *(pp 47–49, section 3.1, 3.2)* —— The first reference is to the old edition
> pp 53–56, section 3.2, 3.3 —— The second reference is to the new edition

Where material is new to the new specification there is no reference to the old edition textbooks.
- **Worked examples** showing you how to tackle a problem and lay out your answer
- **Exercises** with references showing you which exercises in the *Edexcel GCSE Maths* Intermediate core textbook contain similar questions. The first reference, in brackets and italic, is to the old edition. The second reference is to the new edition
- **A summary of key points** so you can check that you have covered all the key concepts

> **Which edition am I using?**
>
> The new editions of the *Edexcel GCSE Maths* core textbooks have yellow cover flashes saying "ideal for the 2001 specification". You can also use the old edition (no yellow cover flash) to help you prepare for your Stage 1 exam.

Exam practice and using the answers

An exam style practice paper at the back of the book will help you make sure that you are totally exam-ready. This paper is exactly the same length and standard as your actual Stage 1 exam.

Answers to all the questions are provided at the back of the book. Once you have completed an exercise you can use the answers to check whether you have made any mistakes. You need to show full working in your exam – it isn't enough to write down the answer.

Contents

Heinemann Educational Publishers,
Halley Court, Jordan Hill, Oxford, OX2 8EJ
part of Harcourt Education
Heinemann is a registered trademark of Harcourt Education Limited

First published 2001

10-digit ISBN: 0 435535 40 4
13-digit ISBN: 978 0 435535 40 7

05
10   9   8

Designed and typeset by Tech-Set Ltd, Gateshead, Tyne and Wear
Cover photo: Digitalvision
Cover design by Miller, Craig and Cocking
Printed in the United Kingdom by Scotprint

Acknowledgements
The publishers and authors would like to thank Jean Linsky for her assistance with the manuscript.

The answers are not the responsibility of Edexcel.

Author team	Publishing team	Design	Production
Karen Hughes	**Editorial**	Phil Richards	David Lawrence
Trevor Johnson	Sue Bennett	Colette Jacquelin	Jason Wyatt
Peter Jolly	Lauren Bourque		
David Kent	Des Brady		
Keith Pledger	Carol Harris		
	Maggie Rumble		
	Nick Sample		
	Harry Smith		

Tel: 01865 888058 www.heinemann.co.uk

1 Integers and powers

1.1 Integers and place value

Teaching reference: (*pp 1–2, section 1.1*) pp 1–2, section 1.1

■ An integer is any positive or negative whole number. Zero is also an integer.

■ Each digit has a value that depends on its position in a number. This is its place value.

Example 1
Which of the following numbers are integers?

　　30,　0.3,　−3,　0,　−3.3

30, −3 and 0 are integers.
0.3 and −3.3 are not whole numbers.

Example 2
(a) Write 2467 381 in words.
(b) Write five hundred and forty thousand two hundred and sixteen in digits.

(a) 2467 381 is

millions	thousands	hundreds	tens	units
2	467	3	8	1

　　Two million, four hundred and sixty seven thousand three hundred and eighty one.
(b) 540 216.

Exercise 1A　　　　　　　　　　　Links (*1A*) 1A

1 From each list of numbers write down the integers:
　(a) 6.3,　63,　−6.3,　−63,　0.
　(b) 562,　5.62,　−5620,　−0.562.
　(c) 1 million,　0.01,　−2,　30 000,　−2.3.

2 Write the following numbers in words:
　(a) 432　　　　　　　　(b) 8200
　(c) 6370　　　　　　　(d) 16 892
　(e) 372 859　　　　　　(f) 483 002
　(g) 3215 468　　　　　(h) 3000 682

3 Write the following numbers in digits:
　(a) four hundred and sixty three
　(b) fifteen thousand and twenty seven
　(c) one hundred and sixteen thousand two hundred and twenty five
　(d) three hundred and five thousand one hundred and one
　(e) two million, three hundred and twenty seven thousand and thirty five
　(f) half a million.

1.2 Long multiplication and long division

Teaching reference:
pp 6–7, section 1.4

Example 3

Work out 278×42.

```
        2 7 8
   ×     4 2
        5 5 6  ─────────── This is 278 × 2.
      1 1
 + 1 1 3 3 2 0  ─────────── This is 278 × 40, which is 278 × 10 × 4.
   1 1 6 7 6  ─────────── This is 278 × 2 + 278 × 40.
```

Example 4

Work out $901 \div 17$.

Method 1

17 divides into 90
5 times remainder 5.

17 divides into 51
3 times exactly.

```
                     5                53
 17)901        17)901          17)901
                  − 85               85↓
                   ──                ──
                    5                51
                                     51
                                     ──
                                     00
```

Method 2

This is a shorter way of setting out the steps in Method 1.

```
        5 3
 17)9 0 ⁵1
```

$$\begin{array}{r} 5\,3 \\ 17\overline{)9\,0\,^5 1} \end{array}$$

Exercise 1B   Links (*1E*) 1E

Do not use a calculator for this exercise.

1   Work out
   (a) 582×13 **(b)** 681×43
   (c) 892×17 **(d)** 634×72
   (e) 307×25 **(f)** 809×20

2   Work out
   (a) $386 \div 16$ **(b)** $952 \div 17$
   (c) $903 \div 21$ **(d)** $782 \div 22$
   (e) $968 \div 14$ **(f)** $876 \div 19$

1.3 Negative numbers

Teaching reference:
(*pp 7–12, section 1.5*)
pp 7–12, section 1.5

■ You can use negative numbers to describe quantities such as temperatures less than **0 °C**.
You can also use negative numbers in calculations.

■ Subtracting a positive number is the same as adding the negative number. Subtracting a negative number is the same as adding the positive number.

■ When you multiply or divide two numbers together this table shows the signs you get:

+	×/÷	+	=	+
+	×/÷	−	=	−
−	×/÷	+	=	−
−	×/÷	−	=	+

Example 5

Work out

(a) $2 - +3$
(b) $-3 - -2$
(c) $4 + -2$
(d) $-3 + +1$

(a) $2 - +3$ is the same as $2 + -3$.
Start at 2: go down 3 to get to -1.
$$2 - +3 = -1$$

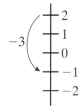

(b) $-3 - -2$ is the same as $-3 + +2$.
Start at -3 and go up 2 to get to -1.
$$-3 - -2 = -1$$

(c) $4 + -2$
Start at 4 and go down 2 to get to $+2$.
$$4 + -2 = 2$$

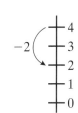

(d) $-3 + +1$
   Start at -3 and go up 1 to get to -2.
   $$-3 + +1 = -2$$

Example 6

Work out

(a) 15×-3 (b) $-8 \div -2$
(c) -16×-3 (d) $-10 \div 5$

(a) $15 \times -3 = -45$ (b) $-8 \div -2 = +4$
(c) $-16 \times -3 = +48$ (d) $-10 \div 5 = -2$

Exercise 1C Links (*1F, 1G, 1H, 1I, 1J*) 1F, 1G, 1H, 1I, 1J

Do not use a calculator for this exercise.

1   Work out
   (a) $-4 + -3$ **(b)** $9 - +5$ **(c)** $8 - -2$
   (d) $5 + +4$ **(e)** $-7 - -6$ **(f)** $-2 + +4$
   (g) $6 + -8$ **(h)** $-3 - +7$

2   Work out
   (a) -3×-8 **(b)** -5×3 **(c)** $24 \div -3$
   (d) $-36 \div -12$ **(e)** -8×5 **(f)** $-48 \div 8$
   (g) 6×-5 **(h)** $-50 \div -5$

3   A diver dives to a depth of -27 metres, surfaces and then dives to a depth of -16 metres. What is the difference in the depths of the dives?

4   The temperature at the Arctic circle is recorded as $-18\,°C$ one night. The following day it rises by $6\,°C$. What is the temperature during the day?

5   Copy and complete the following tables:

(a)

1st number

	×	−2	6	−7
	5		30	
2nd number	−3			
	8	−16		

(b)

1st number

	−	2	−3	8
	−4			
2nd number	5		−8	
	−1			

(c)

1st number

	+	−3	−4	2
	5	2		
2nd number	1			
	−6			

(d)

1st number

	÷	16	−24	−36
	−2		12	
2nd number	4			
	−8			

1.4 Rounding to 1 significant figure and estimating

Teaching reference:
(*pp 74–76, sections 6.4, 6.5*)
pp 76–79, sections 6.4, 6.5

■ The first significant figure is the first non-zero digit in a number, counting from the left.

■ To estimate answers round all numbers to 1 significant figure and do the simpler calculation.

Example 7

Estimate the answer to $\dfrac{563 \times 2140}{25}$.

First round all the numbers to 1 significant figure:

563   to 1 sig. fig. $= 600$

This digit is
greater than 5
so round up.

2140   to 1 sig. fig. $= 2000$

This digit is
less than 5
so round down.

25   to 1 sig. fig. $= 30$

This digit is
5 so round up.

So an estimate would be $\dfrac{600 \times 2000}{30}$

$$= 40\,000$$

Exercise 1D   Links (*6D, 6E*) 6D, 6E

1   Write the following numbers to 1 significant figure:
   (a) 36   (b) 237   (c) 5584   (d) 3.21
   (e) 16.8   (f) 8500   (g) 2159   (h) 3841

2   For each of the following calculations
   (i)   write down a calculation that can be used to estimate the answer,
   (ii) work out an estimated answer.

Do not use a calculator for this question.

   (a) 37×42 (b) $83 \div 18$ (c) $237 \div 39$

   (d) 457×28 (e) $\dfrac{876 \times 15}{12}$ (f) $\dfrac{29 \times 23}{11 \times 27}$

3 43 238 spectators watched a pop concert. They each paid £18 for a ticket. Estimate the total income from the ticket sales.

4 There are 1.76 pints in 1 litre. Estimate how many pints there are in 19 litres.

1.5 Squares, cubes, square and cube roots

Teaching reference:
(*pp 179–181, sections 14.2, 14.3, 14.4*)
pp 217–220, sections 14.2, 14.3, 14.4, 14.5

■ **Square numbers are the result of multiplying a whole number by itself.**

3×3 **can be written as**
3 squared
the square of 3
3^2

■ **Cube numbers are the result of multiplying a whole number by itself then multiplying again.**

$3 \times 3 \times 3$ **can be written as**
3 cubed
the cube of 3
3^3

■ **To square a number multiply the number by itself.**
■ **If** $x \times x = A$ **then** x **is the square root of** A**, written** $\sqrt{A}$**.**
■ **To cube a number multiply the number by itself, then multiply by the number again.**
■ **If** $y \times y \times y = A$ **then** y **is the cube root of** A**, written** $\sqrt[3]{A}$**.**

Example 8
Work out
(a) 3.2^2 (b) 5.1^3
(c) $\sqrt{64}$ (d) $\sqrt[3]{8}$
(e) $\sqrt[3]{-1.331}$

(a) $3.2 \times 3.2 = 10.24$
(b) $5.1 \times 5.1 \times 5.1 = 132.651$
(c) $\sqrt{64} = 8$ or -8 because $8 \times 8 = 64$
             and also $-8 \times -8 = 64$
(d) $\sqrt[3]{8} = 2$ because $2 \times 2 \times 2 = 8$
(e) $\sqrt[3]{-1.331} = -1.1$ because $-1.1 \times -1.1 \times -1.1 = -1.331$

Exercise 1E   Links (*14A, 14B, 14C*) 14B, 14C, 14D

1 Write down the first 5 square numbers.
2 Write down the first 5 cube numbers.

3   Write down the value of

(a) 2.1^2

(b) 3.3^3

(c) $\sqrt{5.76}$

(d) $\sqrt[3]{42.875}$

(e) 14 squared

(f) 10 cubed

(g) the positive square root of 961

(h) the cube of 17

(i) the cube root of 64

(j) 152^2

(k) $\sqrt{625}$

(l) $\sqrt[3]{-216}$

(m) the square of -15

(n) 21.3 squared

(o) $\sqrt{0.36}$

(p) the negative square root of 0.81

(q) 1^2

(r) 1^3

(s) $\sqrt[3]{-1}$

(t) the negative square root of 1.

1.6 BIDMAS

Teaching reference:
(*pp 291–300, sections 21.2–21.5*)
pp 324–332, sections 21.2–21.5

■   **BIDMAS is a made-up word to help you remember the order of operations:**

$$\mathbf{B\ I\ D\ M\ A\ S}$$

Brackets   **Indices**   **Divide**   **Multiply**   **Add**   **Subtract**
                  (powers
                  and roots)

■   **When operations are the same you do them in the order they appear.**

Example 9

Work out

(a) $6 + 3 \times 4$

(b) $\dfrac{48 - 16}{4^2}$

(c) $(2^2 + 3^2) \div 2$

(a) $6 + \underline{3 \times 4}$
   $= 6 + 12$
   $= 18$

(b) $\dfrac{48 - 16}{4^2}$

This line acts as a bracket.

   $(48 - 16) \div 4^2$
   $= 32 \div 4^2$
   $= 32 \div 16$
   $= 2$

(c) $(2^2 + 3^2) \div 2$
   $= ((2 \times 2) + (3 \times 3)) \div 2$
   $= (4 \ + \ 9) \div 2$
   $= \qquad 13 \div 2$
   $= 6.5$

Exercise 1F

1   Work out
   (a) $5 + 4 \times 7$ **(b)** $8 - 8 \div 2$
   (c) $(6 + 2) \times 3$ **(d)** $(5 + 3) \times (6 - 4)$
   (e) $\dfrac{9 \times 3}{5 \times 2}$ **(f)** $(2 + 7)^2$
   (g) $\sqrt{(5 + 4)}$ **(h)** $3^2 + 7$
   (i) $\dfrac{\sqrt{(5 + 20)}}{3 + 2}$ **(j)** $\dfrac{6^2}{\sqrt{9} \times 2}$
   (k) $(5 + 4)^2 - (3 - 5)^2$ **(l)** $8 + 2^2 \times 3 \div (10 - 6)$

2   Make these expressions correct by replacing the $*$ with $+$, $-$,
   $\times$ or $\div$. Use brackets if you need to.
   (a) $3 * 4 * 5 = 27$ **(b)** $2 * 3 * 2 * 3 = 25$
   (c) $6 * 7 * 8 * 9 = 1$ **(d)** $10 * 9 * 8 * 7 = 34$
   (e) $3 * 3 * 3 = 0$ **(f)** $3 * 3 * 3 = 2$

1.7 LCM, HCF and prime factor decomposition

Teaching reference:
(*pp 178, 185–186, sections 14.1, 14.8, 14.9, 14.10*)
pp 216–217, section 14.1;
pp 223–224, sections 14.8, 14.9, 14.10

■   **The factors of a number are whole numbers that divide
exactly into the number. The factors include 1 and the
number itself.**

■   **Multiples of a number are the results of multiplying the
number by a positive whole number.**

■   **A prime number is a whole number greater than 1 which only
has two factors: itself and 1.**

■   **A number written as a product of prime numbers is written in
prime factor form.**

■   **The highest common factor (HCF) of two numbers is the
highest factor common to both of them.**

■   **The lowest common multiple (LCM) of two numbers is the
lowest number that is a multiple of both of them.**

Example 10
(a) Write 36 in prime factor form.
(b) Find the highest common factor (HCF) of 36 and 12.
(c) Find the lowest common multiple (LCM) of 3 and 4.

(a) $36 = 2 \times 18$
                $= 2 \times 2 \times 9$
                $= 2 \times 2 \times 3 \times 3$

which can be simplified to $2^2 \times 3^2$.

(b) Write each number in prime factor form:

$$36 = 2 \times 2 \times 3 \times 3$$
$$24 = 2 \times 2 \times 2 \times 3$$

Pick out the factors common to both numbers. These are

$$2 \times 2 \times 3$$

So the HCF of 24 and 36 is $2 \times 2 \times 3 = 12$.

(c) Write a list of multiples for each number:

3, 6, 9, **12**, 15
4, 8, **12**, 16

The LCM is the lowest number that appears in both lists.
So the LCM of 3 and 4 is 12.

Exercise 1G   Links (*14A, 14G*) 14A, 14G

1 Write down all the factors of
   (a) 48   (b) 360   (c) 29   (d) 100
   (e) 71   (f) 645
2 Write down the numbers in question **1** that are prime numbers.
3 Write down the first 5 multiples of
   (a) 4   (b) 7   (c) 11   (d) 20
4 Write the following in prime factor form (simplify your answers):
   (a) 50   (b) 72   (c) 450   (d) 840
5 Find the HCF of
   (a) 9 and 15   (b) 4 and 14   (c) 12 and 20
   (d) 6, 15 and 21   (e) 8, 24 and 36.
6 Find the LCM of
   (a) 6 and 8   (b) 5 and 7   (c) 4 and 6
   (d) 2, 3 and 4   (e) 5, 6 and 10.

Exercise 1H   Mixed questions

1 A list of numbers is written below:

256 214
256.214
0
three hundred and two thousand four hundred and twelve
−73 864

From the list
(a) write down the integers,
(b) write down the first number in words,
(c) write the fourth number in digits.

2 Work out
   (a) 623×17 **(b)** 563×42
   (c) $744 \div 24$ **(d)** $954 \div 18$

Do not use a calculator in questions **2–6**.

3 Work out
   (a) $-6 + -3$ **(b)** $7 - -3$
   (c) $8 - +4$ **(d)** $-3 + +5$

4 Work out
   (a) -8×2 **(b)** $-10 \div -5$
   (c) $6 \div -3$ **(d)** -7×-5

5 For each of the following calculations
   (i) write down a calculation that could be used to estimate the answer,
   (ii) write down the estimated answer.

   (a) $\dfrac{281 \times 18}{497}$ **(b)** $\dfrac{2.4 \times 7.9}{1.8^2}$

   (c) $\dfrac{8130 \div 381}{\sqrt[3]{7.6}}$

6 Estimate the cost of 27 books at £19.95 each.

7
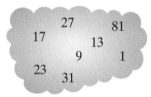

   From the numbers in the cloud write down
   (a) the square numbers
   (b) the cube numbers
   (c) the prime numbers
   (d) factors of 27
   (e) multiples of 3.

8 Write down the value of
   (a) 5^2 **(b)** the square of 10
   (c) 4 cubed   **(d)** $\sqrt[3]{64}$
   (e) $\sqrt{36}$ **(f)** 2^3
   (g) 6.3 squared   **(h)** the cube of 2.4
   (i) the positive square root of 5.76
   (j) $\sqrt[3]{-8}$

9 Use BIDMAS to work out the value of

Do not use a calculator in this question.

   (a) $(7 - 3) \times (5 + 3)$ **(b)** $\dfrac{100}{4 \times 5}$

   (c) $(2 + 5)^2 \div (9 - 2)$ **(d)** $5 + 3^2 \times 2 \div (3 - 9)$

10 Write in prime factor form
   (a) 180   **(b)** 196   **(c)** 600

11 Find the highest common factor (HCF) of
   (a) 12 and 18   **(b)** 42 and 24   **(c)** 6, 12 and 15.

12 Find the lowest common multiple (LCM) of
   (a) 4 and 5   **(b)** 6 and 8   **(c)** 2, 6 and 8.

Summary of key points

- An integer is any positive or negative whole number. Zero is also an integer.

- Each digit has a value that depends on its position in a number. This is its place value.

- You can use negative numbers to describe quantities such as temperatures less than 0 °C.
  You can also use negative numbers in calculations.

- Subtracting a positive number is the same as adding the negative number. Subtracting a negative number is the same as adding the positive number.

- When you multiply or divide two numbers together this table shows the signs you get:

+	×/÷	+	=	+
+	×/÷	−	=	−
−	×/÷	+	=	−
−	×/÷	−	=	+

- The first significant figure is the first non-zero digit in a number, counting from the left.

- To estimate answers round all numbers to 1 significant figure and do the simpler calculation.

- Square numbers are the result of multiplying a whole number by itself.

- Cube numbers are the result of multiplying a whole number by itself then multiplying again.

- To square a number multiply the number by itself.

- If $x \times x = A$ then x is the square root of A, written $\sqrt{A}$.

- To cube a number multiply the number by itself, then multiply by the number again.

- If $y \times y \times y = A$ then y is the cube root of A, written $\sqrt[3]{A}$.

- BIDMAS is a made-up word to help you remember the order of operations:

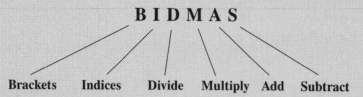

  Brackets   Indices   Divide   Multiply   Add   Subtract

- When operations are the same you do them in the order they appear.

- The factors of a number are whole numbers that divide exactly into the number. The factors include 1 and the number itself.

- Multiples of a number are the results of multiplying the number by a positive whole number.

- A prime number is a whole number greater than 1 which only has two factors: itself and 1.

- A number written as a product of prime numbers is written in prime factor form.

- The highest common factor (HCF) of two numbers is the highest factor common to both of them.

- The lowest common multiple (LCM) of two numbers is the lowest number that is a multiple of both of them.

2 Fractions and decimals

■ In a fraction:

This number shows how many parts we have.

The top number is called the *numerator*.

$$\frac{3}{4}$$

The bottom number is called the *denominator*.

This number shows the total number of parts.

2.1 Equivalent fractions and simplifying fractions

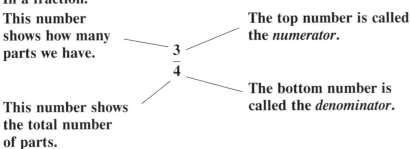

The diagram is divided into 8 parts. 4 parts are shaded. This can be written as $\frac{4}{8}$.

The shaded area is also $\frac{2}{4}$ of the rectangle or $\frac{1}{2}$ of the rectangle.

$\frac{4}{8}, \frac{2}{4}$ and $\frac{1}{2}$ represent the same area of the rectangle.

They are called equivalent fractions.

■ **A fraction can be simplified if the numerator (top) and denominator (bottom) have a common factor.**

■ **To write a fraction in its simplest form divide the numerator and denominator by their highest common factor.**

Example 1

(a) Complete $\dfrac{2}{3} = \dfrac{}{6} = \dfrac{8}{}$

(b) Write these fractions in their simplest form:

(i) $\dfrac{10}{16}$ (ii) $\dfrac{24}{36}$

(a)

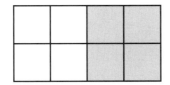

$\dfrac{2}{3} = \dfrac{}{6} = \dfrac{8}{}$ so $\dfrac{2}{3} = \dfrac{4}{6} = \dfrac{8}{12}$

(b) (i) The highest common factor of 10 and 16 is 2:

$$\frac{10}{16} = \frac{5}{8}$$

(ii) The HCF of 24 and 36 is 12:

$$\frac{24}{36} = \frac{2}{3}$$

Exercise 2A   Links (*11B*, *11C*) 11B, 11C

1   Copy and complete these sets of equivalent fractions:

(a) $\dfrac{1}{3} = \dfrac{}{6} = \dfrac{}{12} = \dfrac{}{18}$

(b) $\dfrac{2}{5} = \dfrac{}{10} = \dfrac{}{50} = \dfrac{40}{}$

(c) $\dfrac{3}{8} = \dfrac{6}{} = \dfrac{}{32} = \dfrac{24}{}$

(d) $\dfrac{3}{10} = \dfrac{}{50} = \dfrac{30}{} = \dfrac{}{1000}$

2   Write these fractions in their simplest form:

(a) $\frac{2}{4}$ (b) $\frac{6}{10}$ (c) $\frac{8}{12}$ (d) $\frac{30}{50}$

(e) $\frac{10}{12}$ (f) $\frac{24}{30}$ (g) $\frac{15}{25}$ (h) $\frac{28}{35}$

(i) $\frac{18}{27}$ (j) $\frac{35}{42}$

2.2 Improper fractions and mixed numbers

■ $\frac{5}{2}$ is called an *improper* fraction.

■ $2\frac{1}{2}$ is called a *mixed number*.

■   **Mixed numbers can be written as improper fractions and improper fractions can be written as mixed numbers.**

Example 2

Write as an improper fraction

(a) $2\frac{1}{2}$ (b) $3\frac{1}{4}$

(a) 2 can be written as $\frac{4}{2}$.

So $2\frac{1}{2} = \frac{4}{2} + \frac{1}{2} = \frac{5}{2}$

(b) 3 can be written as $\frac{12}{4}$.

So $3\frac{1}{4} = \frac{12}{4} + \frac{1}{4} = \frac{13}{4}$.

Example 3
Change these improper fractions into mixed numbers:

(a) $\frac{23}{8}$ (b) $\frac{13}{5}$

(a) Arrange $\frac{23}{8}$ into as many groups of $\frac{8}{8}$ ($\frac{8}{8}=1$) as possible:

$$\frac{23}{8}=\frac{8}{8}+\frac{8}{8}+\frac{7}{8}=2\frac{7}{8}$$

(b) $\frac{13}{5}=\frac{5}{5}+\frac{5}{5}+\frac{3}{5}=2\frac{3}{5}$

Exercise 2B Links (*11D*, *11E*) 11D, 11E

1 Write these mixed numbers as improper fractions:

(a) $1\frac{1}{2}$ (b) $1\frac{1}{4}$ (c) $1\frac{2}{5}$ (d) $2\frac{1}{3}$ (e) $3\frac{3}{4}$

(f) $4\frac{3}{5}$ (g) $6\frac{5}{9}$ (h) $8\frac{3}{10}$ (i) $10\frac{7}{8}$ (j) $10\frac{5}{28}$

2 Write these improper fractions as mixed numbers:

(a) $\frac{7}{2}$ (b) $\frac{9}{4}$ (c) $\frac{17}{8}$ (d) $\frac{16}{5}$ (e) $\frac{13}{2}$

(f) $\frac{23}{10}$ (g) $\frac{23}{5}$ (h) $\frac{32}{6}$ (i) $\frac{42}{20}$ (j) $\frac{30}{4}$

2.3 Adding and subtracting fractions

Teaching reference:
(*pp 144–147, section 11.5*)
pp 182–185, section 11.5

■ **To add or subtract fractions find equivalent fractions that have the same denominator.**

Example 4
Work out

(a) $1\frac{1}{2}+2\frac{1}{4}$ (b) $3\frac{1}{3}-1\frac{3}{4}$

(a)
$$1\frac{1}{2}+2\frac{1}{4}=3+\frac{1}{2}+\frac{1}{4}$$
$$=3+\frac{2}{4}+\frac{1}{4}$$
$$=3\frac{3}{4}$$

(b)
$$3\frac{1}{3}-1\frac{3}{4}=2+\left(\frac{1}{3}-\frac{3}{4}\right)$$
$$=2+\left(\frac{4}{12}-\frac{9}{12}\right)$$ You cannot subtract $\frac{9}{12}$ from $\frac{4}{12}$.
$$=1+\left(\frac{16}{12}-\frac{9}{12}\right)$$
$$=1\frac{7}{12}$$

Exercise 2C Links (*11I*, *11J*) 11I, 11J

In this exercise write your answers in their simplest form. Do not use a calculator.

1 Work out

(a) $\frac{1}{2}+\frac{3}{4}$ (b) $\frac{2}{5}+\frac{1}{3}$ (c) $\frac{4}{9}-\frac{1}{4}$ (d) $\frac{6}{7}-\frac{3}{14}$

(e) $\frac{3}{5}+\frac{7}{10}$ (f) $\frac{3}{4}-\frac{2}{7}$ (g) $\frac{3}{7}+\frac{1}{4}$ (h) $\frac{7}{8}-\frac{3}{4}$

2   Work out

   (a) $1\frac{1}{4} + \frac{1}{2}$ **(b)** $2\frac{2}{3} + \frac{5}{6}$ **(c)** $3\frac{2}{3} + \frac{5}{12}$ **(d)** $1\frac{1}{6} + 2\frac{1}{3}$

   (e) $2\frac{3}{5} + 3\frac{4}{15}$ **(f)** $2\frac{5}{6} + 3\frac{3}{4}$ **(g)** $1\frac{1}{2} + 3\frac{2}{7}$ **(h)** $3\frac{2}{7} + 2\frac{1}{3}$

3   Work out

   (a) $1\frac{3}{4} - \frac{1}{8}$ **(b)** $2\frac{5}{6} - \frac{3}{4}$ **(c)** $2\frac{5}{8} - 1\frac{1}{3}$ **(d)** $5\frac{9}{10} - 2\frac{1}{5}$

   (e) $3\frac{1}{2} - \frac{3}{4}$ **(f)** $5\frac{2}{5} - \frac{7}{10}$ **(g)** $4\frac{3}{7} - 2\frac{9}{14}$ **(h)** $6\frac{1}{3} - 2\frac{7}{8}$

4   A baby weighs $7\frac{1}{2}$ lb at birth. She puts on $2\frac{3}{4}$ lb in the first month. How much does the baby weigh after one month?

5   Mrs Jewitt buys $2\frac{1}{2}$ kg of potatoes and $1\frac{3}{8}$ kg of carrots. What is the total weight of vegetables that she buys?

6   A piece of material is $2\frac{3}{4}$ metres long. $1\frac{5}{8}$ metres are needed to make a skirt. How much material is left?

7   A crate filled with bananas weighs $8\frac{3}{4}$ kg. The bananas weigh $6\frac{1}{3}$ kg. How much does the crate weigh?

2.4 Multiplying and dividing fractions

Teaching reference:
(*pp 147–150, section 11.6*)
pp 185–188, section 11.6

■   **To multiply two fractions multiply the numerators (tops) then multiply the denominators (bottoms).**

■   **To divide by a fraction: invert the dividing fraction (turn it upside down) and change the division sign to multiplication.**

■   **When you multiply or divide mixed numbers you must change them to improper fractions first.**

Example 5

Work out

(a) $\frac{2}{5} \times \frac{5}{6}$

(b) $\frac{3}{4} \div \frac{4}{5}$

(c) $1\frac{1}{2} \times 2\frac{3}{4}$

(d) $2\frac{1}{3} \div 1\frac{1}{3}$

(a) $\frac{2}{5} \times \frac{5}{6}$

   $= \dfrac{(2 \times 5) \div 5}{(5 \times 6) \div 5}$ Multiply the numerators and denominators and simplify by dividing top and bottom by 5.

   $= \frac{2}{6} = \frac{1}{3}$

(b) $\frac{3}{4} \div \frac{4}{5}$

   $= \frac{3}{4} \times \frac{5}{4}$ Invert the dividing fraction and multiply.

   $= \frac{15}{16}$

(c) $1\frac{1}{2} \times 2\frac{3}{4}$

   $= \frac{3}{2} \times \frac{11}{4}$ Change the mixed numbers into improper fractions.

   $= \dfrac{3 \times 11}{2 \times 4} = \dfrac{33}{8}$ This is an improper fraction; simplify by changing it to a mixed number.

   $= 4\frac{1}{8}$

(d) $2\frac{1}{3} \div 1\frac{1}{3}$

$= \frac{7}{3} \div \frac{4}{3}$ Change the mixed numbers into improper fractions.

$= \frac{7}{3} \times \frac{3}{4}$ Invert the dividing fraction and multiply.

$= \frac{(7 \times 3) \div 3}{(3 \times 4) \div 3}$ Simplify by dividing top and bottom by 3.

$= \frac{7}{4}$ This is an improper fraction, simplify by changing it to a mixed number.

$= 1\frac{3}{4}$

Exercise 2D   Links *(11K, 11L, 11M)* 11K–O

Write all your answers in this exercise in their simplest form. Do not use a calculator.

1 Work out

(a) $\frac{1}{5} \times \frac{2}{3}$ (b) $\frac{1}{4} \div \frac{1}{2}$ (c) $\frac{2}{5} \times \frac{3}{4}$

(d) $\frac{3}{5} \times \frac{5}{6}$ (e) $\frac{5}{8} \div \frac{3}{4}$ (f) $\frac{11}{16} \div \frac{3}{8}$

(g) $\frac{2}{3} \times \frac{6}{11}$ (h) $\frac{5}{12} \times \frac{4}{15}$ (i) $\frac{3}{8} \div \frac{5}{16}$

(j) $\frac{9}{15} \div \frac{12}{25}$

2 Work out

(a) $1\frac{1}{2} \times \frac{3}{4}$ (b) $2\frac{1}{5} \times 1\frac{1}{4}$ (c) $3\frac{1}{6} \times 1\frac{2}{3}$

(d) $4\frac{1}{2} \times 3\frac{3}{5}$ (e) $2\frac{3}{4} \times 1\frac{2}{11}$ (f) $4\frac{2}{5} \times 2\frac{5}{11}$

(g) $5 \times \frac{3}{4}$ (h) $2 \times \frac{3}{8}$

3 Work out

(a) $1\frac{1}{2} \div 1\frac{3}{8}$ (b) $2\frac{2}{5} \div 1\frac{3}{10}$ (c) $3\frac{1}{3} \div 1\frac{5}{6}$

(d) $2\frac{1}{7} \div 1\frac{3}{14}$ (e) $5\frac{1}{2} \div 1\frac{3}{4}$ (f) $6\frac{1}{8} \div \frac{3}{4}$

(g) $3 \div \frac{1}{4}$ (h) $5 \div \frac{3}{8}$

4 A plank of wood is 6 m long. It is cut into lengths, each measuring $\frac{3}{4}$ m. How many lengths can be cut from the plank?

5 A recipe for a fruit cake requires $2\frac{3}{8}$ kg of fruit. How much fruit would be required for 3 cakes?

6 A gardener spends $4\frac{1}{2}$ hours working on a garden. He spends $\frac{1}{3}$ of that time weeding. How much time does the gardener spend weeding?

7 Karen is writing a book. She writes for $10\frac{3}{4}$ hours during a weekend. She takes $3\frac{1}{2}$ hours to write a chapter. How many chapters does she write during the weekend?

2.5 Decimals: place value, multiplying and dividing by powers of 10

Teaching reference:
(*pp 2–4, section 1.2*)
pp 2–4, section 1.2

■ Decimals are used for parts of a number that are smaller than 1.

■ To multiply decimals by 10 move the digits one place to the left. To multiply by 100 move the digits two places to the left.

■ To divide decimals by 10 move the digits one place to the right. To divide by 100 move the digits two places to the right.

Example 6

Write down the answers to

(a) 2.36×10 (b) 3.2×1000
(c) $14.3 \div 100$ (d) $3.6 \div 100$

(a) $2.36 \times 10 = 23.6$ (b) $3.2 \times 1000 = 3200$
(c) $14.3 \div 100 = 0.143$ (d) $3.6 \div 1000 = 0.0036$

Exercise 2E   Links (*1C*) 1B, 1C

Do not use a calculator for this exercise.

1   Write down the answers to
    (a) 5.31×10 (b) $2.16 \div 10$
    (c) $53.58 \div 100$ (d) 2.671×100
    (e) 0.36×10 (f) $5.3 \div 1000$
    (g) 6.38×100 (h) 0.28×1000
    (i) $0.3 \div 100$ (j) $7.86 \div 1000$

2   A book weighs $0.36\,\text{kg}$ and has 100 pages.
    (a) How much will 10 of these books weigh?
    (b) How much does each page weigh?

3   A packet of sweets weighs $113\,\text{g}$. The packet contains 10 sweets. How much does each sweet weigh?

4   How many grams are there in $3.568\,\text{kg}$? ($1\,\text{kg} = 1000\,\text{g}$.)

2.6 Ordering decimals

Example 7

Rearrange these numbers in order of size:
    2.03,   0.23,   0.215,   0.013,   1.23.

2 is bigger than 1. ———⟨ 2.03
                        1.23
1 is bigger than 0. ———⟨ 0.23
                        0.23
⟩——— Hundredths place: 3 is bigger than 1.
0.215
⟩——— Tenths place: 2 is bigger than 0.
0.013

Exercise 2F	Links (*1D*) 1D

1   Rearrange each of these lists of numbers in descending order:
    (a) 0.6, 0.62, 6.2, 0.59.   **(b)** 0.76, 0.79, 7.9, 0.079.
    (c) 3.21, 3.12, 3.27, 0.37.   **(d)** 0.91, 0.09, 1.01, 0.99.
    (e) 0.02, 0.021, 0.024, 0.002.

2   The heights of 4 children, in metres, are shown below:

> Graham   1.68
> Julie   1.60
> Karen   1.67
> Keith   1.52

Rearrange the list in ascending order of height.

3   In an experiment, the times taken for a chemical reaction to
    occur are recorded and given below:

> 3.6 s, 3.62 s, 3.96 s, 3.902 s.

Rearrange these times in ascending order.

2.7 Multiplying and dividing decimal numbers

Teaching reference:
(*pp 2–4 section 1.2*)
pp 2–4, section 1.2

■   **When multiplying decimals: the answer must have
     the same number of decimal places as the total number of
     decimal places in the numbers being multiplied.**

■   **When dividing by a decimal: multiply the number you are
     dividing by by a power of 10 to change it into a whole number.
     Then multiply the number you are dividing into by the same
     power of 10.**

Example 8

Work out 0.08×0.14.

d.p. = decimal place

$$
\begin{array}{r}
14 \\
\times\ 8 \\
\hline
112 \\
\hline
\scriptstyle 3
\end{array}
\qquad
\begin{array}{c}
0.08 \times 0.14 \\
\big|\qquad\big| \\
2\,\text{d.p.} + 2\,\text{d.p.} = 4\,\text{d.p.}
\end{array}
$$

The answer must have 4 d.p., so the answer is 0.0112.

Example 9

Work out $3.25 \div 0.05$.

$$0.05\overline{)\,3.25}$$

$\times$ by 100

$$5\overline{)3\ 2^{2}5} \quad \frac{6\ 5}{}$$

$$3.25 \div 0.05 = 65$$

Exercise 2G   Links 1B, 1C

Do not use a calculator for this exercise.

1 Work out
   (a) 0.3×5 **(b)** 0.6×0.7
   (c) 2.34×0.2 **(d)** 3.67×0.09
   (e) 12.7×0.6 **(f)** 3.93×1.2
   (g) 16.2×3.7 **(h)** 7.12×0.032

2 Work out
   (a) $15.6 \div 6$ **(b)** $209.2 \div 4$
   (c) $28.5 \div 4$ **(d)** $10.56 \div 0.6$
   (e) $2.36 \div 0.8$ **(f)** $58.6 \div 2.5$
   (g) $2.34 \div 0.32$ **(h)** $3.26 \div 0.16$

3 A piece of material 23.4 m long is cut into 5 equal lengths. How long is each of the lengths?

4 Work out the total weight of 8 bags of dried fruit weighing 0.375 kg each.

5 A glass holds $0.3\,l$. How many glasses of coke can be poured from a $1.5\,l$ bottle?

6 A car will travel 17.2 km on 1 litre of petrol. How far will the car travel on 8.5 litres of petrol?

7 How many stamps costing £0.27 can be bought with £4.86?

2.8 Converting between fractions and decimals

■ **You can convert a fraction to a decimal by dividing the numerator by the denominator.**

■ **Not all fractions have an exact decimal equivalent.**

■ **Recurring decimal notation:**
   0.3̇ means 0.333 333 recurring.
   0.1̇7̇ means 0.171 717 recurring.

■ **Terminating decimals can be written as an exact fraction using a place value table.**

Example 10
Change these fractions into decimals:
(a) $\frac{2}{5}$ (b) $\frac{5}{12}$ (c) $\frac{2}{11}$

(a) $2 \div 5 = 0.4$

(b) $5 \div 12 = 0.416\,666 = 0.41\dot{6}$ (the 6 repeats)

(c) $2 \div 11 = 0.181\,818 = 0.\dot{1}\dot{8}$ (both 1 and 8 repeat)

> 0.416 666 7
>
> If you work out $5 \div 12$ on a calculator, the result on the display could be 0.416 666 7. The result has been corrected to 7 s.f. by the calculator.

Example 11

Change these decimals into fractions:
(a) 0.6   (b) 0.148   (c) 0.36

(a) $0.6 = \frac{6}{10}$ This can be simplified by dividing top and bottom by 2.
       $= \frac{3}{5}$

(b) $0.148 = \frac{148}{1000}$ Simplify by dividing top and bottom by 4.
          $= \frac{37}{250}$

(c) $0.36 = \frac{36}{100}$ Simplify by dividing top and bottom by 4.
        $= \frac{9}{25}$

Exercise 2H   Links (*11F, 11G, 11H*) 11F, 11G, 11H

1 Change these fractions into decimals:
   (a) $\frac{3}{5}$ (b) $\frac{1}{6}$ (c) $\frac{5}{8}$ (d) $\frac{9}{20}$ (e) $\frac{3}{4}$
   (f) $\frac{1}{3}$ (g) $\frac{4}{9}$ (h) $\frac{7}{12}$ (i) $\frac{7}{22}$ (j) $\frac{7}{27}$

2 Change these decimals into fractions. Simplify your answers if possible.
   (a) 0.7   (b) 0.5   (c) 0.12   (d) 0.65
   (e) 0.8$\dot{3}$ (f) 0.362   (g) 0.137   (h) 0.685

3 Which of the following fractions have exact decimal equivalents?
   (a) $\frac{4}{5}$ (b) $\frac{5}{9}$ (c) $\frac{7}{25}$ (d) $\frac{4}{13}$ (e) $\frac{8}{17}$

2.9 Ordering decimals and fractions

Example 12

Rearrange in descending order:
   $\frac{3}{4}$, 0.82, 2.68, 3, $\frac{7}{10}$

First write any fractions as decimals.
   $\frac{3}{4} = 0.75$ $\frac{7}{10} = 0.7$

Whole numbers:
3 is bigger than 2. — 3
2 is bigger than 0. — 2.68
0.82 — Tenths place: 8 is bigger than 7.
0.75 — Hundredths place: 5 is bigger than zero.
0.70

   3, 2.68, 0.82, $\frac{3}{4}$, $\frac{7}{10}$.

1 Rearrange each list in ascending order:

(a) $0.81, \frac{13}{25}, \frac{8}{10}, 0.84, 0.7$.

(b) $\frac{1}{2}, 0.7, \frac{3}{4}, 0.75, 0.73$.

(c) $2, 2.3, 2\frac{4}{10}, 2.42, 2\frac{43}{100}$.

(d) $\frac{3}{10}, 0.33, \frac{1}{3}, 0.34, \frac{7}{20}$.

(e) $4, 4\frac{4}{9}, 4.04, 4\frac{4}{10}, 4.44$.

2 Rearrange the measurements in the following lists in ascending order of size:

(a) The weights of quadruplets at birth were 1.3 kg, 1.32 kg, 1.41 kg, 1.39 kg.

(b) The times taken for five 100 metre runners to complete a race were 10.1 s, 10.01 s, 9.92 s, 10.11 s, 9.9 s.

(c) The weights of 4 bags of apples are $\frac{1}{4}$ kg, 0.3 kg, $\frac{1}{2}$ kg, 0.35 kg.

(d) The widths of 4 drill bits are $\frac{3}{8}$ inch, $\frac{1}{4}$ inch, $\frac{1}{6}$ inch, $\frac{2}{5}$ inch.

2.10 Converting between metric and imperial units

■ You need to be able ato convert between metric and imperial units.

■ You should learn these conversions.

	Metric	Imperial
*	1 Kilogram (1 kg)	2.2 lb
	25 grams	1 ounce
*	1 litre (1 l)	$1\frac{3}{4}$ pints
*	4.5 litres (4.5 l)	1 gallon
*	8 kilometres (8 km)	5 miles
*	1 metre (1 m)	39 inches
	2.5 centimetres (2.5 cm)	1 inch

You need to know the starred items (*) for your examination.

Example 13

Change 20 km to miles

8 kilometres = 5 miles (approximately – taken from the table)

so 1 kilometre = $\frac{5}{8}$ miles

so 20 kilometres = $20 \times \frac{5}{8} - 20 \times 0.625$

= 12.5 miles (approximately)

Exercise 2J

1 Convert:
   (a) 10 litres to pints   **(b)** 30 pints to litres

2 Convert:
   (a) 5 kilograms to pounds   **(b)** 44 lbs to kilograms

3 A computer screen is 17 inches wide.
   Work out the width of the screen in centimetres.

4 A car travels 30 miles in 1 hour.
   Change 30 miles to kilometres.

5 A car hold 12.5 gallons of petrol.
   Convert 12.5 gallons into litres.
   Give your answer correct to one decimal place.

Exercise 2K   Mixed questions

1 Copy and complete:
   (a) $\frac{1}{2} = \frac{}{8}$ **(b)** $\frac{3}{4} = \frac{12}{}$ **(c)** $\frac{5}{8} = \frac{}{24}$

2 Write these fractions in their simplest form:
   (a) $\frac{10}{15}$ **(b)** $\frac{27}{33}$ **(c)** $\frac{42}{56}$ **(d)** $\frac{36}{48}$

3 Write these mixed numbers as improper fractions:
   (a) $1\frac{3}{4}$ **(b)** $2\frac{2}{7}$ **(c)** $3\frac{5}{8}$

4 Write these improper fractions as mixed numbers:
   (a) $\frac{8}{5}$ **(b)** $\frac{13}{6}$ **(c)** $\frac{25}{7}$

5 **(a)** $\frac{5}{8} + \frac{2}{3}$ **(b)** $\frac{3}{4} - \frac{2}{5}$ **(c)** $2\frac{1}{4} + 3\frac{2}{5}$
   (d) $2\frac{1}{3} - 1\frac{1}{4}$ **(e)** $2\frac{3}{7} + 1\frac{5}{6}$ **(f)** $3\frac{1}{8} - 1\frac{3}{4}$

> Do not use a calculator for questions **5–16**.

6 Rebecca buys $1\frac{1}{4}$ kg of apples, $\frac{1}{2}$ kg of grapes and $\frac{3}{4}$ kg of bananas. How much fruit does she buy altogether?

7 Pamela has some maths and geography homework. She spends $2\frac{1}{4}$ hours doing her homework. The geography homework takes her $1\frac{1}{2}$ hours. How long does she spend on her maths homework?

8 **(a)** $\frac{4}{5} \times \frac{5}{8}$ **(b)** $\frac{2}{3} \div \frac{5}{6}$ **(c)** $2\frac{1}{4} \times 1\frac{2}{3}$
   (d) $1\frac{1}{2} \div 5\frac{1}{4}$ **(e)** $2\frac{2}{3} \div 1\frac{1}{8}$ **(f)** $1\frac{3}{5} \times 2\frac{3}{4}$

9 The total lesson time in 1 day in a particular secondary school is $4\frac{1}{2}$ hours. Each lesson is $\frac{3}{4}$ hour. How many lessons are there in the school day?

10 A litre of water is about the same as $1\frac{3}{4}$ pints. Approximately how many pints of water are there in $3\frac{1}{2}$ litres?

11 Write down the answers to:
(a) $31.3 \div 10$ (b) 4.38×10 (c) $2.56 \div 100$
(d) 0.2×100 (e) $5.6 \div 1000$ (f) 2.13×1000

12 A packet of biscuits weighs 0.375 kg. How much will a case of 100 packets of biscuits weigh?

13 1000 sheets of paper weigh 6.8 kg. How much does 1 sheet of paper weigh?

14 Work out
(a) 3.28×1.3 (b) $4.84 \div 1.1$
(c) 2.6×32.1 (d) $0.576 \div 0.16$

15 A packet of cornflakes contains 0.45 kg of cornflakes. A serving of cornflakes is 0.03 kg. Calculate the number of servings in the packet.

16 Material costs £1.36 a metre. Calculate the cost of 5.6 metres of material.

17 Change these fractions into decimals:
(a) $\frac{4}{5}$ (b) $\frac{7}{8}$ (c) $\frac{5}{9}$

18 Change these decimals into fractions in their simplest form:
(a) 0.16   (b) 0.6   (c) 0.485

19 Rearrange these lists of numbers in descending order:
(a) $3.3, \frac{3}{4}, 0.3, 3, \frac{3}{8}$.
(b) $\frac{7}{10}, 0.\dot{7}, \frac{3}{4}, 0.77, \frac{37}{50}$.

20 Convert a distance of
(a) 40 kilometres into miles
(b) 120 miles into kilometres.

21 A car holds 15 gallons of petrol.
Change 15 gallons into litres.

Summary of key points

■ **In a fraction:**

This number shows how many parts we have. —— $\dfrac{3}{4}$ —— **The top number is called the *numerator*.**

This number shows the total number of parts. —— **The bottom number is called the *denominator*.**

- A fraction can be simplified if the numerator (top) and denominator (bottom) have a common factor.

- To write a fraction in its simplest form divide the numerator and denominator by their highest common factor.

- $\frac{5}{2}$ is called an *improper* fraction.

- $2\frac{1}{2}$ is called a *mixed number*.

- Mixed numbers can be written as improper fractions and improper fractions can be written as mixed numbers.

- To add or subtract fractions find equivalent fractions that have the same denominator.

- To multiply two fractions multiply the numerators (tops) then multiply the denominators (bottoms).

- To divide by a fraction: invert the dividing fraction (turn it upside down) and change the division sign to multiplication.

- When you multiply or divide mixed numbers you must change them to improper fractions first.

- Decimals are used for parts of a number that are smaller than 1.

- To multiply decimals by 10 move the digits one place to the left. To multiply by 100 move the digits two places to the left.

- To divide decimals by 10 move the digits one place to the right. To divide by 100 move the digits two places to the right.

- When multiplying decimals: the answer must have the same number of decimal places as the total number of decimal places in the numbers being multiplied.

- When dividing by a decimal: multiply the number you are dividing by by a power of 10 to change it into a whole number. Then multiply the number you are dividing into by the same power of 10.

- You can convert a fraction to a decimal by dividing the numerator by the denominator.

- Not all fractions have an exact decimal equivalent.

- Recurring decimal notation:

  $0.\dot{3}$ means 0.333 333 recurring.

  $0.\dot{1}\dot{7}$ means 0.171 717 recurring.

- Terminating decimals can be written as an exact fraction using a place value table.

■ **You should learn these conversions.**

Metric	Imperial
*	1 Kilogram (1 kg)	2.2 lb
	25 grams	1 ounce
*	1 litre (1 l)	$1\frac{3}{4}$ pints
*	4.5 litres (4.5 l)	1 gallon
*	8 kilometres (8 km)	5 miles
*	1 metre (1 m)	39 inches
	2.5 centimetres (2.5 cm)	1 inch

3 Percentages

3.1 Percentages, fractions and decimals

Teaching reference:
(*pp 312–314, section 22.1*)
pp 346–348, section 22.1

■ percent
  %   } means 'out of 100'.
  pc

■ To change a percentage to a fraction write as a fraction with a denominator of 100.

■ To change a percentage to a decimal, first change it to a fraction and then to a decimal.

■ To change a decimal to a percentage multiply the decimal by 100%.

■ To change a fraction to a percentage, first change the fraction to a decimal then multiply by 100%.

Example 1

Write these percentages as (i) decimals (ii) fractions:

(a) 35%   (b) $37\frac{1}{2}\%$

(a) (i) $35\% = \frac{35}{100} = 35 \div 100 = 0.35$

    (ii) $35\% = \frac{35}{100} = \frac{7}{20}$

(b) (i) $37\frac{1}{2}\% = \frac{37\frac{1}{2}}{100} = 37.5 \div 100 = 0.375$

    (ii) $37\frac{1}{2}\% = \frac{37\frac{1}{2}}{100} = \frac{75}{200} = \frac{3}{8}$

Example 2

Write as percentages
(a) 0.75   (b) $\frac{4}{25}$
(c) 0.175   (d) $\frac{5}{8}$

(a) $0.75 \times 100\% = 75\%$

(b) $\frac{4}{25} = 4 \div 25 = 0.16 \qquad 0.16 \times 100\% = 16\%$

(c) $0.175 \times 100\% = 17.5\%$

(d) $\frac{5}{8} = 5 \div 8 = 0.625 \qquad 0.625 \times 100\% = 62.5\%$

Exercise 3A	Links (*22A, 22B*) 22A, 22B

1 Write these percentages as (**i**) decimals (**ii**) fractions:
    (**a**) 65%   (**b**) 20%   (**c**) 25%   (**d**) 32%
    (**e**) 74%   (**f**) $22\frac{1}{2}\%$ (**g**) $67\frac{1}{2}\%$ (**h**) $33\frac{1}{3}\%$
    (**i**) $66\frac{2}{3}\%$ (**j**) $5\frac{1}{4}\%$

2 Write as percentages
   (a) $\frac{1}{2}$ **(b)** 0.6   **(c)** 0.23   **(d)** $\frac{7}{20}$
   (e) 0.85   **(f)** $\frac{3}{10}$ **(g)** 0.575   **(h)** $\frac{9}{40}$
   (i) 0.0225   **(j)** $\frac{5}{6}$

3 Copy and complete this table:

Fraction	Decimal	Percentage
		15%
$\frac{7}{10}$		
	0.32	
$\frac{7}{8}$		
		$16\frac{2}{3}\%$

3.2 Finding a percentage of a quantity

Teaching reference:
(*pp 315–317, section 22.2*)
pp 349–351, section 22.2

■ **To find a percentage of a quantity, change the percentage to a fraction or a decimal and multiply it by the quantity.**

Example 3
Work out
(a) 40% of 80   (b) $22\frac{1}{2}\%$ of £50

(a) 40% of 80 $= \frac{40}{100} \times 80 = 32$

(b) $22\frac{1}{2}\%$ of £50 $= \frac{22\frac{1}{2}}{100} \times £50 = \frac{45}{200} \times £50 = £11.25$

Exercise 3B   Links (*22D*) 22D

1 Work out
   (a) 30% of 90   **(b)** 70% of 60   **(c)** 55% of 20
   (d) 25% of 36   **(e)** 18% of £10   **(f)** 36% of £25
   (g) $17\frac{1}{2}\%$ of £50   **(h)** $52\frac{1}{2}\%$ of 500 kg   **(i)** $33\frac{1}{3}\%$ of 30 g
   (j) $66\frac{1}{3}\%$ of £27

2 In a school there are 150 pupils in Year 11. Girls make up 52% of the pupils. Find
   (a) the number of girls in Year 11,
   (b) the number of boys in Year 11.

3 A yogurt contains 6% fat. Work out how many grams of fat there will be in a yogurt weighing 175 g.

4 Lucy earns £10 500 a year. She pays 22% tax.
   How much tax does Lucy pay on her earnings?

5   A book has 240 pages. 35% of the pages are printed in colour.
     The rest are printed in black and white only.
     How many pages in the book are black and white only?

6   A ticket for a concert costs £27. The performer is paid $16\frac{2}{3}\%$ of
     the price of the ticket.

     How much does the performer receive from each ticket sold?

7   An author is paid $12\frac{1}{2}\%$ royalties for each of her books sold.
     Her book is sold for £12.
     How much does the author receive in royalties per book?

3.3 Percentage increase and decrease

■   **To increase a quantity by a percentage find the percentage of**
     the quantity and add it to the original quantity.

■   **To decrease a quantity by a percentage find the percentage of**
     the quantity and subtract it from the original quantity.

Teaching reference:
(*p 316, section 22.2*)
pp 350–351, section 22.2

Example 4

Phil earns £15 000 per year. He receives a 5% pay increase. Work
out his new earnings.

   5% of £15 000 $= \frac{5}{100} \times$ £15 000 $=$ £750

His earnings have been increased, so his new earnings are

   £15 000 $+$ £750 $=$ £15 750

Example 5

In the first year of ownership a car's value depreciates by 12%.
Work out the value of a car after 1 year if it costs £8000 when new.

   12% of £8000 $= \frac{12}{100} \times$ £8000 $=$ £960

Depreciation means decrease so the value of the car after 1 year is

   £8000 $-$ £960 $=$ £7040

Exercise 3C   Links (*22E*) 22E

1   (a) Work out the sale price of the Leggit trainers.
     (b) Work out the sale price of the Strut tracksuit.

SALE
25% off
normal prices

Leggit trainers
Normal price
£42.

Strut tracksuit
Normal price
£68.

2 A discount warehouse advertises a sofa as £400 + VAT. The rate of VAT is $17\frac{1}{2}$%. Work out the total cost of the sofa.

3 Mr and Mrs Jones buy a house for £40 000. Two years later they sell it, making a profit of 12%.
How much did they sell their house for?

4 Keith wants to buy some tiles for his patio. The normal cost of the tiles is £330. Keith is offered a 10% discount if he pays in cash. How much will the tiles cost if Keith pays for them in cash?

5 The money in a savings account earns 6% interest per year. Rebecca puts £240 into the account at the start of the year. How much will Rebecca have in her savings account after 1 year?

6 Karen buys a new car. The car costs £14 000. After 3 years the value of the car has depreciated by 18%.
What is the value of Karen's car after 3 years?

7 Miss Addison earns a salary of £18 500. She is given a pay rise equal to the annual rate of inflation for that year. The annual rate of inflation for that year is $2\frac{1}{2}$%.
Calculate Miss Addison's new salary.

8

Videos
£230 + VAT
@ $17\frac{1}{2}$

Calculate the cost of a video.

3.4 Finding a quantity as a percentage of another

■ **To write one quantity as a percentage of another:**
  1 Write one quantity as a fraction of the other.
  2 Change the fraction to a decimal.
  3 Multiply the decimal by 100%.

■ **When a quantity changes (increases or decreases) find the percentage change using**

$$\text{percentage change} = \frac{\text{actual change}}{\text{original quantity}} \times 100\%$$

Example 6
In a box of 20 chocolates, 12 chocolates were soft centred.
What percentage of the chocolates were soft centred?
  1 Write the quantities as a fraction: $\frac{12}{20}$
  2 Change the fraction to a decimal: $\frac{12}{20} = 12 \div 20 = 0.6$
  3 Multiply the decimal by 100%: $0.6 \times 100\% = 60\%$.
60% of the chocolates were soft centred.

Example 7

A shopkeeper buys apples at £1.50 per kilo. He sells them for £1.62 per kilo.
Calculate his percentage profit.

$$\text{percentage change (profit)} = \frac{\text{actual change}}{\text{original quantity}} \times 100\%$$

The original price is £1.50.
The actual profit is £0.12.

$$\text{percentage profit} = \frac{£0.12}{£1.50} \times 100\%$$
$$= 8\%$$

Exercise 3D   **Links (22F) 22F**

1   Graham scored 36 out of 40 in a spelling test.
    Write this as a percentage.

2   A pet food manufacturer claims that 8 out of 10 cats prefer
    their cat food.
    What percentage of cats is this?

3   In a village of 2500 there are 650 children, 960 men and 890
    women. What percentage of the people in the village are
    (a) children
    (b) men
    (c) women?

4   Out of a flock of 150 sheep, 100 gave birth to twin lambs and
    the rest gave birth to single lambs.
    What percentage of the flock gave birth to
    (a) twin lambs
    (b) single lambs?

5   The weight of a chocolate bar is increased from 60 g to 72 g.
    Calculate the percentage increase in weight of the chocolate
    bar.

6   The cost of a DVD player fell from £440 to £363.
    Calculate the percentage decrease in the cost of the DVD
    player.

7   The normal price of a jumper is £50. In a sale it is sold for
    £37.50. Calculate the percentage reduction in the price of the
    jumper.

8   A carpenter makes kitchen tables. They cost him £240 to
    make. He sells them for £288.
    Calculate his percentage profit.

9   After Christmas a supermarket sells off its left-over Christmas cakes. The Christmas cakes were bought by the supermarket for £3.20, and sold off at £2.
Calculate the percentage loss.

10 In 2000 the cost of a skiing holiday was £450. In 2001 the same holiday cost £549.
Calculate the percentage increase of the cost of the holiday.

Exercise 3E   Mixed questions

1   Copy and complete this table:

Fraction	Decimal	Percentage
$\frac{3}{5}$		
		24%
	0.325	
$\frac{5}{6}$		

2   Work out
    (a) 80% of 30
    (b) 24% of £10
    (c) $12\frac{1}{2}$% of £48
    (d) $66\frac{2}{3}$% of 90 g.

3   80 girls enter a ballet examination. 85% of the girls pass the exam. Write down the number of girls who
    (a) pass the exam
    (b) fail the exam.

4   The cost of a television is £360 plus VAT. The rate of VAT is $17\frac{1}{2}$%. Calculate the total cost of the television.

5   A department store offers a 15% discount on all sports equipment on Bank Holiday Monday. A pair of trainers normally costs £44.
Calculate the cost of the pair of trainers on Bank Holiday Monday.

6   Jessica scores 28 out of 35 on her driving theory test.
What percentage is this?

7   Douglas buys a computer for £500. Two years later he sells it for £175. Calculate his percentage loss.

8   The weight of a cereal bar is increased from 80 g to 90 g. The manufacturers claim that this is a 15% increase.
Is the manufacturers' claim justified? Give a reason for your answer.

Summary of key points

■ percent
    %   } means 'out of 100'.
    pc

■ To change a percentage to a fraction write as a fraction with a denominator of 100.

■ To change a percentage to a decimal, first change it to a fraction and then to a decimal.

■ To change a decimal to a percentage multiply the decimal by 100%.

■ To change a fraction to a percentage, first change the fraction to a decimal then multiply by 100%.

■ To find a percentage of a quantity, change the percentage to a fraction or a decimal and multiply it by the quantity.

■ To increase a quantity by a percentage find the percentage of the quantity and add it to the original quantity.

■ To decrease a quantity by a percentage find the percentage of the quantity and subtract it from the original quantity.

■ To write one quantity as a percentage of another:
    1 Write one quantity as a fraction of the other.
    2 Change the fraction to a decimal.
    3 Multiply the decimal by 100%.

■ When a quantity changes (increases or decreases) find the percentage change using

$$\text{percentage change} = \frac{\text{actual change}}{\text{original quantity}} \times 100\%$$

4 Coordinates and the elements of algebra

4.1 Coordinates

Example 1

Give the coordinates of the points that could complete the parallelogram in the diagram:

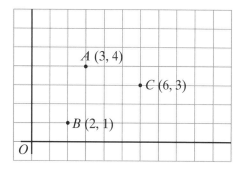

(i)   Suppose BA is a side of the parallelogram.
      This is 1 unit across (x direction) and 3 up (y direction).
      CD must also be 1 across and 3 up.
      D is $(7,6)$.

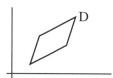

(ii) If AB is the side then A to B is 1 unit backwards and 3 down.
      C to D must also be 1 backwards and 3 down. D is $(5,0)$.

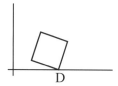

(iii) There is another possibility: CB is a side of the parallelogram.
      C to B is 4 units backwards and 2 down.
      This means D would be $(-1,2)$.

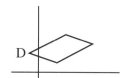

Exercise 4A   **Links 7A**

1   Copy each diagram and find a point to complete an isosceles triangle. Find one where the given line is one of the equal sides and one where it is the unequal side.
    Are there any others?

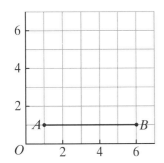 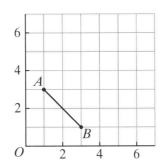 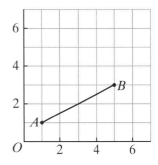

2   Draw axes which run 0–8 for x and 0–6 for y.
    Plot A $(2, 3)$, B $(4, 3)$ and C $(5, 1)$.
    Find 3 points which could complete a parallelogram.

3   Draw axes running from 0 to 6.
    Plot points P $(2, 4)$ and Q $(4, 3)$.
    These are two vertices of a square.
    Find 3 pairs of points which could complete the square.

4   Draw the x-axis to run from 0 to 8 and the y-axis from 0 to 5.
    Plot points A $(7, 1)$, B $(2, 1)$ and C $(1, 3)$.
    Find the coordinates of D to complete trapezium $ABCD$.

5   Draw the x-axis from -10 to $+10$ and the y-axis from -8 to $+6$. Plot points A $(-3, 5)$, B $(-8, 0)$ and C $(-7, -7)$.
    Find the coordinates of D to complete a rhombus.
    Find, also, 4 pairs of integer coordinates that would complete a kite.

4.2 Collect like terms

Teaching reference:
(*pp 297–299, section 21.5*)
pp 328–330, section 21.5

■   **Rules: $a + a + a = 3a$ $a \times a \times a = a^3$ $a \times b = ab$**
    $n(a + b) = na + nb$

Example 2
Simplify $2a - 3b + 5a + b$.

Each term keeps its own sign.

So, rearrange to get $2a + 5a - 3b + b$.

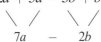

$\qquad\qquad 7a \quad - \quad 2b$

Exercise 4B   **Links 21E**

In each question simplify as fully as possible:

1   $2x + 3x - 4y$ 2 $2a + 3b - 4a$
3   $6p - 3q + 2p - 2q$ 4 $4t + 3s + 7s - 2t$
5   $5c - 4d - 3d - 6c$ 6 $c + 2d + 5c - d$
7   $2ab + 3ab$ 8 $5cd - 2dc$
9   $4pq + 3pq - 2pq$ 10 $a^2 + a + 3a$
11   $5b^2 - 2b + 3b$ 12 $4c^2 - 2c^2 + 3c$
13   $a^3 + 2a^2 + 3a$ 14 $2a + 3ab + 3a + 4b$
15   $2xy - y + 4x - 5x + 3yx + y$

4.3 Expand and simplify

Teaching reference:
(*p 296, section 21.4*)
p 327, section 21.4

Example 3
Simplify $2(3x - y) + 5(y - 2x)$.

$2(3x - y) + 5(y - 2x)$

This is 2 lots of $(3x - y)$ This is 5 lots of $(y - 2x)$.
i.e. $(3x - y) + (3x - y) = 6x - 2y$

or $2 \times (3x - y) = 6x - 2y$ $5 \times (y - 2x) = 5y - 10x$

$6x - 2y + 5y - 10x = 3y - 4x$

Exercise 4C   **Links (*21D, 21E, 21F*)**

Expand and simplify:

1   $3(x + 2) + 2(x + 4)$ 2 $4(2x - 1) + 3(4x + 7)$
3   $5(3x + 2) + 4(2x + 1)$ 4 $7(3 - 2x) + 3(2x - 3)$
5   $6(4 - 2x) - 3(5 + 3x)$ 6 $4(3 - 2x) + 3(1 - 5x)$
7   $2(3x - 5y) + 3(2x - 4y)$ 8 $5(6y + 2x) - 4(3x + 2y)$
9   $3(2x - 3y) - 2(5x + 6y)$ 10 $3(2x + 3y) - 5(x + y)$
11   $4(3y - 2) - 5(y - 2)$ 12 $2(3x + 6) - 3(2x - 5)$
13   $4(3 - 2x) - 3(5 - 3x)$ 14 $2(3 - y - 2x) - 3(4x - 3y)$
15   $3(2x - 3y) + 5(3x - 2y)$ 16 $5(3y - 5x) - 2(x - 3y)$
17   $(4x - 3y) + 2(3x - 2y)$ 18 $7(3x - 5y) - (x - 3y)$
19   $x(2y + 1) + 2x(3y + 1)$ 20 $2x(3y + 1) + y(2x + 1)$
21   $2y(3x - 2) + 3x(2 - 3y)$ 22 $4x(2y - 5x) + 2y(x - 3y)$

23 $3a(b-2a)+2b(3a-2b)$

24 $4p(2q+3p)+3p(2p+q)$

25 $5c(3c+2d)-2c(c-d)$

26 $3c(2d-4c)-3c(c-5d)$

27 $a(a+b)+b(a+b)$

28 $2a(3b+c)-b(a+c)-c(a+b)$

29 $3a(b+c)+2b(a+c)+c(2a+3b)$

30 $2a(b-2c)-3b(2a+3c)$

4.4 Factorizing

Example 4

Factorize $2a^2+6ab$.

This has 2 terms: $2a^2$ and $6ab$.

2 and a are factors of each term so $2a$ is a common factor.

Answer: $2a^2+6ab=2a(a+3b)$.

Exercise 4D   **Links (21J) 21J**

Factorize:

1	$3x+12$	**2**	$7x-21$	**3**	$15x+20$
4	$9x-12$	**5**	$4x+6$	**6**	$9x-15$
7	$12x+18$	**8**	$21+28x$	**9**	$14+21y$
10	$35x-15$	**11**	$6x-3y$	**12**	$14x+7y$
13	$10x-5y$	**14**	$25a+15b$	**15**	$3a-9b$
16	$17p+51q$	**17**	$36c-9d$	**18**	$24s+16t$
19	x^2+6xy	**20**	$2x^2-3xy$	**21**	$4xy+y^2$
22	$5ab-a^2$	**23**	$6bc+b^2$	**24**	$4b^2+5bc$
25	$3ab-5bc$	**26**	$2x^2+6xy$	**27**	$3x^2-9xy$
28	$8p^2+4pq$	**29**	$14x^2+21xy$	**30**	$10ab-15bc$
31	$4a^2-6abc$	**32**	$2x^3+4x^2y$		

4.5 Algebraic language

Teaching reference:
(*pp 175, 291, 301, 412–414*)
pp 213, 323, 332–333, 460–462

■ **An equation can be recognised from the = sign.**

■ **A formula is an equation with two or more variables. They usually start with a subject e.g. $V = l \times w \times h$**

■ **An identity is when both sides of an equation are identical when both sides are fully simplified. e.g. $3x^2 + 6x = 3x(x + 2)$**

■ **A term is a single item separated from other items by $+, -, =, <,$ or $>$.**

$$2a^2 + 3ab > (a^3 + 2b)$$

first   second   The brackets make
term.   term.   this the third term.

■ **An expression is one or more terms together without a relation like $=, >, <$.**

Exercise 4E   **Links (*13D, 21A, 28B*) 13D, 21A, 28B**

Select the correct word from 'equation', 'formula', 'identity', 'expression' to describe the following:

(a) $2x + 1 = 7$

(b) $3 - 3x = 9$

(c) $15 + 7x$

(d) $p = 2at$

(e) $v = ut$

(f) $\frac{1}{2}at^2$

(g) $2x(x + 3) = 2x^2 + 6x$

(h) $y(2y + 3) = 2y^2 + 3y$

4.6 Substitute into formulae

Example 5

The formula for the surface area of a sphere is $A = 4\pi r^2$. Work out
(a) the surface area of a sphere with radius 6 cm
(b) the radius of a sphere with surface area 500 cm².

(a) $A = 4\pi \times 6^2 = 4 \times \pi \times 36 = 452.4 \text{ cm}^2$
(b) $500 = 4 \times \pi \times r^2$
$$r^2 = 500 \div 4\pi = 39.788\,73$$
$$r = 6.31 \text{ cm}$$

Teaching reference:
(*pp 301–307, sections 21.6, 21.7*)
pp 333–340, sections 21.6, 21.7

The number 6 replaces the letter r. A substitute is a replacement.

Exercise 4F   **Links (*21H*) 21H**

1   $F = 1.8C + 32$ is a formula which links temperatures in degrees Fahrenheit (F) with temperatures in degrees Celsius (C).
   (a) Use the formula to convert
      (i) 20 °C   (ii) 45 °C   (iii) 70 °C into °F.
   (b) Use the formula to convert
      (i) 212 °F   (ii) 122 °F   (iii) 77 °F into °C.

2   The cost, C, in £, of having t trees and b bushes together with delivery is given by the formula
$$C = 10t + 6b + 15$$

Greg has £315 to spend and needs 35 bushes. How many trees can he afford?

3 $A = \frac{1}{2}bh$ is the formula for working out the area of a triangle.
Work out the area of a triangle when
(a) $b = 30$ cm, $h = 20$ cm
(b) $b = 15$ cm, $h = 26$ cm
(c) $b = 7.3$ cm, $h = 2.9$ cm
(d) $b = 23$ mm, $h = 1.3$ cm.

4 $V = \frac{1}{3}\pi r^2 h$ is the formula for finding the volume of a cone.
Work out the volume of a cone with
(a) $r = 5$ cm, $h = 10$ cm
(b) $r = 7$ cm, $h = 15$ cm
(c) $r = 4.6$ cm, $h = 92$ mm.

5 $v = u + at$ is a formula for finding the speed of an object.
Find v when
(a) $u = 6$, $a = 10$ and $t = 5$
(b) $u = 8$, $a = -10$ and $t = 6$
(c) $u = 20$, $a = -32$ and $t = 4\frac{1}{2}$.

Exercise 4G   Mixed questions

1   Simplify fully
(a) $a + 3a$ (b) $2b - 3b + 5b$
(c) $2c - 3d + c - d$ (d) $6p - 3q - 5p - 2q$
(e) $3x + 2y - 3y - 4x$

2   Expand and simplify
(a) $3(2a - 5x)$ (b) $a(a^2 + 2ab)$
(c) $2b(c - 5d)$ (d) $3b(2b + 2a)$
(e) $3x(2x - xy)$

3   Factorize
(a) $16x - 12$ (b) $8a^2 + 12b$
(c) $6x^2 + 9xy$ (d) $a^2b - b^2a$
(e) $3p^2q + 15pq$

4 $s = ut + \frac{1}{2}at^2$ is a formula for working out the distance, s,
moved by an object.
Work out s when
(a) $u = 4$, $a = 10$, $t = 3$
(b) $u = 5$, $a = -10$, $t = 5$
(c) $u = -3$, $a = -32$, $t = 6$.

5   Equation, formula, expression, identity.
Select the word from the above list which describes each of the
following:
(a) $P = 2(a + b)$ (b) $x(2x + y) = 2x^2 + xy$
(c) $\pi r^2 h$ (d) $2x + 5 = 13$
(e) $D = M/V$ (f) $2\pi r$

Summary of key points

- $a + a + a = 3a$

  $a \times a \times a = a^3$

  $a \times b = ab$

  $n(a + b) = na + nb$

- An equation can be recognised from the $=$ sign.

- A formula is an equation with two or more variables. They usually start with a subject e.g. $V = l \times w \times h$

- An identity is when both sides of an equation are identical when both sides are fully simplified. e.g.
  $3x^2 + 6x = 3x(x + 2)$

- A term is a single item separated from other items by $+, -, =, <, >$.

  $$2a^2 + 3ab > (a^3 + 2b)$$

  first term.   second term.   The brackets make this the third term.

- An expression is one or more terms together without a relation like $=, >, <$.

5 Algebraic equations

Teaching reference:
(pp 412–414, sections 28.1, 28.2)
pp 16–17, section 2.2;
pp 20–21, section 2.6;
pp 460–462, sections 28.1, 28.2

5.1 Solving equations using inverse operations

■ The *inverse* of an operation is the opposite operation.
■ You can solve some types of equation using inverse operations.

$+ 4$ is the inverse of $- 4$.
$\times 5$ is the inverse of $\div 5$.

Example 1

Solve the equation $5a - 3 = 27$ using inverse operations.

Draw the number machine for $a \rightarrow 5a - 3$.

Draw the inverse number machine for $a \rightarrow 5a \rightarrow 3$.

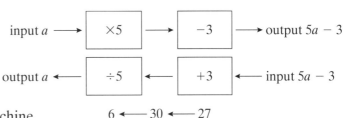

Send 27 through the inverse number machine.
The solution is $a = 6$.

Example 2

Solve the equation $\dfrac{b + 5}{3} = 4$ using

inverse operations.

Draw the number machine

for $b \rightarrow \dfrac{b + 5}{3}$.

Draw the number machine for the

inverse of $b \rightarrow \dfrac{b + 5}{3}$.

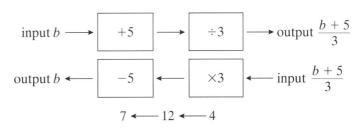

Send 4 through the inverse number machine.
The solution is $b = 7$.

Exercise 5A   Links (28B) 2C, 2I, 28A

Solve these equations using inverse operations:

1 $a + 6 = 15$ **2** $4b = 16$ **3** $\dfrac{c}{3} = 5$

4 $4d + 5 = 17$ **5** $7e - 5 = 16$ **6** $\dfrac{f - 4}{6} = 2$

7 $4(g + 2) = 32$ **8** $\dfrac{h}{4} + 6 = 11$ **9** $\dfrac{m + 1}{4} = 3$

10 $6(n - 1) = 30$ **11** $2p + 3 = 10$ **12** $\dfrac{q + 7}{2} = 3$

13 $\dfrac{t}{5} + 7 = 7$ **14** $9v - 1 = 2$ **15** $3(x + 5) = 6$

16 $4(y - 2) = 3$ **17** $\dfrac{a}{3} + 6 = 2$ **18** $8b + 9 = 9$

19 $2(3c - 1) = 22$ **20** $\dfrac{3d + 11}{2} = 4$

5.2 Solving equations by balancing

Teaching reference:
(*pp 415–419, section 28.3*)
pp 463–467, section 28.3

■ To rearrange an equation you can
  - add the same quantity to both sides
  - subtract the same quantity from both sides
  - multiply both sides by the same quantity
  - divide both sides by the same quantity.

■ Whatever you do to one side of an equation you must do to the other side. This is called the *balance* method.

■ You can solve most linear equations using the balance method, including any which can be solved using inverse operations.

Example 3
Solve the equation $6p + 7 = 31$ using the balance method.

$6p + 7 = 31$
$6p = 24$ (-7)
$p = 4$ $(\div 6)$

Example 4
Solve the equation $3(q - 4) = 15$ using the balance method.

$3(q - 4) = 15$
$3q - 12 = 15$ (expand brackets)
$3q = 27$ $(+12)$
$q = 9$ $(\div 3)$

Alternative method for solving $3(q - 4) = 15$:
Divide both sides by 3:
  $q - 4 = 5$
Add 4 to both sides:
  $q = 9$

Example 5
Solve the equation $\dfrac{t - 7}{4} = 2$ using the balance method.

$\dfrac{t - 7}{4} = 2$
$t - 7 = 8$ $(\times 4)$
$t = 15$ $(+7)$

Exercise 5B   **Links (*28C, 28D*) 28C**

Solve these equations using the balance method:

1 $a - 5 = 7$ **2** $6b = 30$

3 $\dfrac{c}{6} = 4$ **4** $3d - 5 = 16$

5 $5(e + 2) = 40$ **6** $\dfrac{f + 4}{5} = 4$

7 $4g + 5 = 29$ **8** $\dfrac{h}{3} - 5 = 2$

9 $7(m - 4) = 21$ **10** $\dfrac{n - 3}{6} = 2$

11 $9p - 1 = 2$ **12** $6(q + 5) = 30$

13 $\dfrac{t + 10}{6} = 1$ **14** $5v + 3 = 7$

15 $\dfrac{x}{3} + 7 = 5$ **16** $3(y - 1) = 2$

17 $3a + 5 = 2$ **18** $2(b - 3) = 3$

19 $\dfrac{3c + 4}{3} = 2$ **20** $3(2d - 5) = -27$

5.3 Equations with the unknown on both sides

Teaching reference:
(*pp 415–419, section 28.3*)
pp 463–467, section 28.3

■ **You can use the balance method to solve equations with the unknown on both sides.**

Example 6
Solve the equation $5x - 7 = 3x + 9$ using the balance method.

$$5x - 7 = 3x + 9$$
$$2x - 7 = 9 \qquad (-3x)$$
$$2x = 16 \qquad (+7)$$
$$x = 8 \qquad (\div 2)$$

Example 7
Solve the equation $7y + 9 = 4(y - 3)$ using the balance method.

$$7y + 9 = 4(y - 3)$$
$$7y + 9 = 4y - 12 \qquad \text{(expand)}$$
$$3y + 9 = -12 \qquad (-4y)$$
$$3y = -21 \qquad (-9)$$
$$y = -7 \qquad (\div 3)$$

Exercise 5C   Links (*28E, 28F*) 28D, 28E

Solve these equations using the balance method:

1 $3a + 5 = 2a + 9$ **2** $8b - 1 = 5b + 8$

3 $7(c - 3) = 2c + 9$ **4** $5(d + 2) = 3(d + 8)$

5 $3d - 1 = 9d - 13$ **6** $5e + 6 = 3e + 7$

7 $4(f - 1) = 7f + 8$ **8** $5(n - 1) = 2(n + 3)$

9 $5(p - 6) = 3(p - 10)$ **10** $4(q - 2) = 9q + 1$

5.4 Equations with negative coefficients

■   **The coefficient is the number in front of the unknown.**

■   **You can use the balance method to solve linear equations with negative coefficients.**

Teaching reference:
(*pp 415–419, section 28.3*)
pp 463–467, section 28.3

In $4 - 3x$ the coefficient of x is -3.

Example 8

Solve the equation $7 - 3x = 19$ using the balance method.

$$7 - 3x = 19$$
$$7 = 3x + 19 \qquad (+3x)$$
$$3x = -12 \qquad (-19)$$
$$x = -4 \qquad (\div 3)$$

Alternative method:
Subtract 7 from both sides:
$$-3x = 12$$
Divide both sides by -3:
$$x = -4$$

Example 9

Solve the equation $4 + 3x = 9 - 2x$ using the balance method.

$$4 + 3x = 9 - 2x$$
$$4 + 5x = 9 \qquad (+2x)$$
$$5x = 5 \qquad (-4)$$
$$x = 1 \qquad (\div 5)$$

You could subtract $3x$ from both sides
$$4 = 9 - 5x$$
but positive coefficients are easier to work with.

Example 10

Solve the equation $4 - 3x = 7 - 5x$ using the balance method.

$$4 - 3x = 7 - 5x$$
$$4 + 2x = 7 \qquad (+5x)$$
$$2x = 3 \qquad (-4)$$
$$x = 1\tfrac{1}{2} \qquad (\div 2)$$

You could add $3x$ to both sides
$$4 = 7 - 2x$$
but it is safer to get rid of negative coefficients.

Exercise 5D   Links (*28D, 28E*) 28D, 28E

Solve these equations using the balance method.

1 $8 - x = 6$ **2** $9 - 2x = 1$

3 $10 - 3x = 1$ **4** $3x + 2 = 10 - x$

5 $4(x + 1) = 11 - 3x$ **6** $9 - 2x = x$

7 $9 - 5x = 3x + 1$ **8** $2 - x = 10 - 3x$

9 $1 - 6x = 9 - 7x$ **10** $5 - 6x = 9 - 8x$

11 $3 - 4x = 8 - 9x$ **12** $17 - 6x = 5 - 3x$

13 $3 - 4x = 15$ **14** $7 - 6x = 7$

15 $8 - 2x = 3$ **16** $5 + 2x = 8 - 3x$

17 $8 + 3x = 1 - 4x$ **18** $5(4 - x) = 5 + 4x$

19 $13 - 2x = 3 - 7x$ **20** $3 - 9x = 5 - 6x$

5.5 Using equations to solve problems

Teaching reference:
(*pp 415–419, section 28.3*)
pp 463–467, section 28.3

■ **You can use equations to solve problems.**

Example 11

I think of a number. I multiply it by 3 and add 14 to the result. The answer is the same as when I multiply the number by 5 and subtract 4.
What number did I think of?

Let x stand for the number.

Then
$$
\begin{aligned}
3x + 14 &= 5x - 4 \\
14 &= 2x - 4 \quad (-3x) \\
2x &= 18 \quad (+4) \\
x &= 9 \quad (\div 2)
\end{aligned}
$$

The number is 9.

Example 12

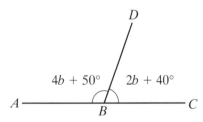

In the diagram, ABC is a straight line.
Find the size of angle ABD.

Use the fact that the sum of the angles on a straight line is $180°$ to write down an equation in b.

$$
\begin{aligned}
4b + 50 + 2b + 40 &= 180 \\
6b + 90 &= 180 \quad \text{(simplify)} \\
6b &= 90 \quad (-90) \\
b &= 15 \quad (\div 6)
\end{aligned}
$$

When $b = 15$, $4b + 50 = 4 \times 15 + 50 = 110$
angle $ABD = 110°$

1   I think of a number. I multiply it by 7 and subtract 9. The result is 47. Find the number.

2   The sizes of the angles of a triangle are $a + 30°$, $a + 40°$ and $a - 10°$. Find the size of the largest angle of the triangle.

3   I think of a number. I multiply it by 3 and subtract the result from 50. The answer is 14. Find the number.

4

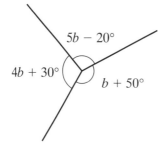

The diagram shows three angles at a point. Find the size of each of the angles.

5   The lengths, in centimetres, of the sides of a triangle are $3x - 4$, $x + 5$ and $15 - 2x$. The perimeter of the triangle is 24 cm. Find the length of each of its sides.

6   I think of a number. I multiply it by 7 and subtract 6 from the result. The answer is the same as when I multiply the number by 4 and add 27 to the result. Find the number.

7   The length of each side of a square is $2y - 5$ centimetres. The perimeter of the square is 36 cm. Find the value of y.

8   Gwen is 39 years older than her son. She is also 4 times as old as he is. Find Gwen's age.

9   The length of a rectangle is 3 cm greater than its width. The perimeter of the rectangle is 54 cm. Find its length.

10

$$6x - 9$$

$5y - 7$ $25 - 3y$

$$2x + 15$$

The diagram shows a rectangle. Find the values of x and y.

5.6 Equations with fractions

■ **To solve equations with algebraic fractions, first clear the denominators by multiplying both sides of the equation by the lowest common multiple of the denominators.**

Teaching reference:
(*pp 415–419, section 28.3*)
pp 463–467, section 28.3

Example 13

Solve the equation $\dfrac{d}{8} + 6 = \dfrac{d-2}{3}$.

The lowest common multiple of 8 and 3 is 24.
So multiply both sides of the equation by 24:

$$\frac{d}{8} + 6 = \frac{d-2}{3}$$

$$24\left(\frac{d}{8} + 6\right) = 24\left(\frac{d-2}{3}\right) \qquad (\times 24)$$

$$24\left(\frac{d-2}{3}\right)$$

$$= \frac{24}{3}(d-2)$$

$$= 8(d-2)$$

$$= 8d - 16$$

$3d + 144 = 8d - 16$	(remove brackets)
$144 = 5d - 16$	$(-3d)$
$5d = 160$	$(+16)$
$d = 32$	$(\div 5)$

Exercise 5F   **Links (28F) 28F**

1 $\dfrac{a}{5} + 2 = \dfrac{a}{4}$

2 $\dfrac{b}{3} - 1 = \dfrac{b}{6} + 3$

3 $\dfrac{c+2}{5} - 4 = 1$

4 $\dfrac{d}{2} + \dfrac{d}{3} = 15$

5 $\dfrac{3e-5}{4} = 7$

6 $\dfrac{m}{6} + 7 = \dfrac{m+8}{2} - 3$

7 $\dfrac{3n-1}{4} = \dfrac{2n+5}{3}$

8 $\dfrac{p+4}{2} = \dfrac{p-3}{3} + 5$

9 $3(y-4) = \dfrac{y}{2} + 3$

10 $2(z+1) = \dfrac{4z-5}{3} + 9$

11 $\dfrac{q+3}{5} = \dfrac{q}{4} + 1$

12 $\dfrac{t-1}{3} + 5 = \dfrac{t}{9} + 7$

13 $\dfrac{8-3v}{5} = 2$

14 $\dfrac{13-4w}{3} = w + 2$

15 $\dfrac{13-2x}{3} = 4 - x$

16 $\dfrac{9-4y}{2} = 5 - 3y$

17 $\dfrac{1-4z}{3} = \dfrac{2z+3}{2}$

18 $\dfrac{2x-1}{8} + \dfrac{x+3}{4} = 1$

19 $\dfrac{2y+1}{2} + \dfrac{y-3}{5} = 2$

20 $\dfrac{3x-1}{5} - \dfrac{2x-3}{4} = 2$

5.7 Quadratic equations

■ A quadratic equation is one in which the highest power of x is x^2.

■ You can solve some simple quadratic equations using inverse operations.

■ The inverse operation of 'square' is 'find the square root<u>s</u>'.

■ A quadratic equation usually has two solutions.

Teaching references:
(*pp 240–243, sections 18.2, 18.3, 18.4, 18.5*)
pp 277–285, sections 18.2, 18.3, 18.4, 18.5

$x^2 + 4 = 29$, $3x^2 - 6 = 42$ and $25x^2 = 9$ are quadratic equations.

The square root of 36 can be 6 or −6 because $6 \times 6 = 36$ and $-6 \times -6 = 36$.

Example 14

Solve the quadratic equation $x^2 + 4 = 29$.

This is the number machine for $x \rightarrow x^2 + 4$ with the inverse number machine.

Send 29 through the inverse number machine.

The solutions are $x = 5$ or $x = -5$, which is usually written as $x = \pm 5$.

Alternatively, you could show the steps like this:

$$x^2 + 4 = 29$$
$$x^2 = 25 \quad (-4)$$
$$x = \pm 5 \quad \text{(square roots)}$$

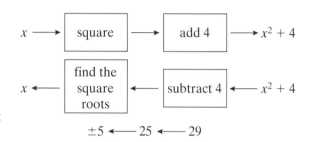

Example 15

Solve the quadratic equation $3x^2 - 6 = 42$.

This is the number machine for $x \rightarrow 3x^2 - 6$ with the inverse number machine.

Send 42 through the inverse number machine.

The solutions are $x = \pm 4$.

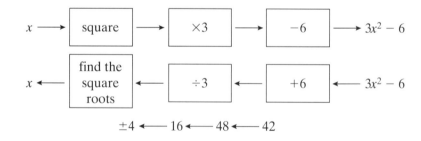

Example 16

Solve the quadratic equation $25x^2 = 9$.

This is the number machine for $x \rightarrow 25x^2$ with the inverse number machine.

Send 9 through the inverse number machine.

The solutions are $x = \pm \frac{3}{5}$.

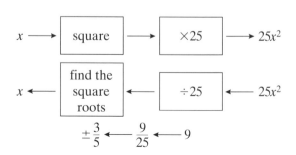

Exercise 5G   Links (*18C*) 18C

1 $x^2 + 1 = 50$ 2 $x^2 - 7 = 57$ 3 $3x^2 = 75$

4 $8x^2 = 72$ 5 $\dfrac{x^2}{3} = 12$ 6 $4x^2 + 5 = 41$

7 $7x^2 + 3 = 31$ 8 $x^2 = \dfrac{9}{64}$ 9 $x^2 = \dfrac{25}{4}$

10 $4x^2 = 1$ 11 $49x^2 = 9$ 12 $25x^2 = 36$

13 $16x^2 = 1$ 14 $4x^2 = 81$ 15 $25x^2 = 100$

5.8 Equations with the unknown as the denominator

■ **You can use *balancing* to solve equations in which the unknown appears in the denominator.**

This means equations like $\dfrac{20}{a} = 4$ and $\dfrac{2}{t} = 3$.

Example 17

Solve the equation $\dfrac{20}{a} = 4$.

$$\dfrac{20}{a} = 4$$
$$20 = 4a \quad (\times a)$$
$$a = 5 \quad (\div 4)$$

Example 18

Solve the equation $\dfrac{2}{t} = 3$.

$$\dfrac{2}{t} = 3$$
$$2 = 3t \quad (\times t)$$
$$t = \dfrac{2}{3} \quad (\div 3)$$

Exercise 5H   Links 28C

Solve these equations:

1 $\dfrac{28}{a} = 7$ 2 $\dfrac{40}{b} = 5$ 3 $\dfrac{7}{c} = 28$ 4 $\dfrac{5}{d} = 40$

5 $\dfrac{5}{e} = 2$ 6 $\dfrac{2}{p} = 5$ 7 $\dfrac{1}{t} = 5$ 8 $\dfrac{3}{t} = 2$

9 $\dfrac{3}{x} = 8$ 10 $\dfrac{8}{y} = 3$

Exercise 5I   Mixed questions

Solve these equations:

1 $5a - 3 = 12$ 2 $\dfrac{b+7}{3} = 2$

3 $3(c + 2) = 8$ 4 $\dfrac{6d-1}{4} = 5$

5 $6e - 7 = 4e - 3$ 6 $3(f + 1) = 5f - 2$

7 $7(g - 1) = 3(g - 2)$ 8 $7 - 5h = 22$

9 $6m + 7 = 7 - 5m$ 10 $3(n + 2) = 4 - 2n$

11 $14 - 7p = 6 - 5p$ 12 $4(7 - 2x) = 13 - 5x$

13 $\dfrac{y}{6} - 2 = \dfrac{y}{9} + 1$ 14 $\dfrac{z-2}{3} = \dfrac{z+1}{6} - 2$

15 $\dfrac{7 - 4q}{3} = 5$ 16 $\dfrac{17 - 9t}{5} = 3t + 1$

17 $\dfrac{5 - 3u}{4} = \dfrac{7 - 2u}{3}$ 18 $\dfrac{9v - 5}{4} + \dfrac{2v + 1}{3} = 2$

19 $\dfrac{3w + 7}{2} - \dfrac{2w + 5}{4} = 3$ 20 $5a^2 - 3 = 17$

21 $9b^2 = 64$ 22 $\dfrac{24}{c} = 3$

23 $\dfrac{3}{d} = 8$

24 Gordon put only 5p and 10p coins in his money box. The
    number of 10p coins was 3 more than the number of 5p coins.
    The total value of the coins in his money box was £3. Find the
    number of 5p coins. (Hint: work in pence.)

25 The perimeter of a rectangle is 120 cm. The length of the
    rectangle is 4 times its width. Find the length of the rectangle.
    (Hint: let the width of the rectangle be x centimetres.)

Summary of key points

- The *inverse* of an operation is the opposite operation.
- You can solve some types of equation using inverse operations.
- To rearrange an equation you can
  - add the same quantity to both sides
  - subtract the same quantity from both sides
  - multiply both sides by the same quantity
  - divide both sides by the same quantity.
- Whatever you do to one side of an equation you must do to the other side. This is called the *balance* method.

■ You can solve most linear equations using the balance method, including any which can be solved using inverse operations.

■ You can use the balance method to solve equations with the unknown on both sides.

■ The coefficient is the number in front of the unknown.

■ You can use the balance method to solve linear equations with negative coefficients.

■ You can use equations to solve problems.

■ To solve equations with algebraic fractions, first clear the denominators by multiplying both sides of the equation by the lowest common multiple of the denominators.

■ A quadratic equation is one in which the highest power of x is x^2.

■ You can solve some simple quadratic equations using inverse operations.

■ The inverse operation of 'square' is 'find the square roots'.

■ A quadratic equation usually has two solutions.

■ You can use *balancing* to solve equations in which the unknown appears in the denominator.

6 Sequences

6.1 Term to term rules

- A sequence is a succession of numbers formed according to a rule.
- The numbers in a sequence are called the *terms* of the sequence.
- One type of rule for a sequence tells you what to do to each term to obtain the next term in the sequence.

This is called a 'term to term' rule for the sequence.

Example 1

The first term in a sequence is 1. The rule for the sequence is **add 2**.

(a) Find the next three terms in the sequence.
(b) Write down the mathematical name for the numbers in this sequence.

(a)   second term $= 1 + 2 = 3$
      third term $= 3 + 2 = 5$
     fourth term $= 5 + 2 = 7$

    The next three terms are 3, 5, 7.
(b) This is the sequence of **odd** numbers.

Example 2

The first term in a sequence is 3. The rule for the sequence is **multiply by 3**.

(a) Find the next three terms in the sequence.
(b) Write down the mathematical name for the numbers in this sequence.

(a)   second term $= 3 \times 3 = 9$
      third term $= 9 \times 3 = 27$
     fourth term $= 27 \times 3 = 81$

$9 = 3^2$
$27 = 3^3$
$81 = 3^4$

    The next three terms are 9, 27, 81.
(b) This is the sequence of **powers of 3**.

Example 3

The first term in a sequence is 5.
The rule for the sequence is **multiply by 2 then add 3**.
Find the next three terms in the sequence.

    second term $= 5 \times 2 + 3 = 13$
     third term $= 13 \times 2 + 3 = 29$
    fourth term $= 29 \times 2 + 3 = 61$

The next three terms are 13, 29, 61.

■ **To find the rule for a sequence, it is often helpful to find the differences between consecutive terms.**

Example 4

The first five terms of a sequence are 20, 17, 14, 11, 8.
(a) Find the rule for this sequence.
(b) Find the next two terms in the sequence.

(a)   20   17   14   11   8
    differences   3   3   3   3

Each term is 3 less than the one before it and so the rule is **subtract 3**.
(b) The next two terms are 8 − 3 i.e. 5 and 5 − 3 i.e. 2.

Example 5

The first five terms in a sequence are 2, 5, 14, 41, 122.
Find the sixth term.

              2   5   14   41   122
differences   3   9   27   81

Each difference is 3 times the previous difference. So the next difference is 3×81 i.e. 243.

    Sixth term $= 122 + 243 = 365$

> Alternatively, the rule for this sequence is **multiply by 3 then subtract 1**. So
> 6th term $= 3 \times 122 - 1$
> $= 366 - 1 = 365$

Exercise 6A

1 For each of these sequences
  (**a**) find the next three terms in the sequence,
  (**b**) write down the mathematical name for the numbers in the sequence.
      (**i**)   first term $= 2$; rule is **add 2**
      (**ii**) first term $= 5$; rule is **add 5**
      (**iii**) first term $= 2$; rule is **multiply by 2**.

2 Find the next three terms in each of these sequences:
  (**a**) first term $= 19$; rule is **subtract 4**
  (**b**) first term $= 125$; rule is **divide by 5**
  (**c**) first term $= 1$; rule is **multiply by 4 then add 3**
  (**d**) first term $= 7$; rule is **subtract 5 then multiply by 4**
  (**e**) first term $= 56$; rule is **add 8 then divide by 2**.

3 For each of these sequences
  (**a**) find the rule for the sequence,
  (**b**) find the next two terms in the sequence.
      (**i**)   7, 13, 19, 25, 31, ...   (**ii**) 36, 29, 22, 15, ...
      (**iii**) 2, 10, 50, 250, ...   (**iv**) 64, 32, 16, 8, ...

4 For each of these sequences
   (a) find the next two terms in the sequence,
   (b) write down the mathematical name of the numbers in the sequence.
       (i)   9, 18, 27, 36, 45, ...   **(ii)**   10, 100, 1000, 10 000, ...

5 For each of these sequences
   (a) find the rule for the sequence,
   (b) find the next two terms in the sequence.
       (i)   35, 29, 23, 17, 11, ...
       (ii)   10 000, 1000, 100, 10, ...
       (iii) $-13, -10, -7, -4, ...$
       (iv)   64, 16, 4, 1, ...

6 Find the next term for each of these sequences:
   (a) 5, 7, 11, 17, 25, ...   **(b)** 5, 7, 11, 19, 35, ...
   (c) 8, 14, 23, 35, 50, ...   **(d)** 2, 22, 39, 53, 64, ...

7 These patterns of dots show the first five *square* numbers 1, 4, 9, 16, 25:

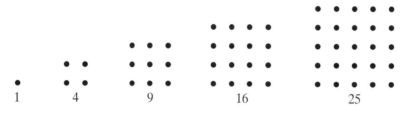

   (a) Find the differences for the first five square numbers.
   (b) Use your answer to **(a)** to write down a rule for the sequence.
   (c) Use your rule to write down the next five square numbers.

8 These patterns of dots show the first five *triangle* numbers.

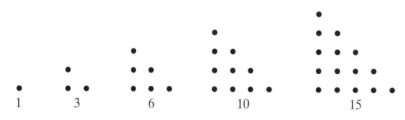

   (a) Find the differences for the first five triangle numbers.
   (b) Use your answer to **(a)** to write down a rule for the sequence.
   (c) Use your rule to write down the next five triangle numbers.

6.2 Position to term rules and *n*th terms

■ **Another type of rule for a sequence tells you what to do to the term number to obtain that term in the sequence.**

Teaching reference:
(*pp 25–27, section 2.9*)
pp 27–29, section 2.9

This is called a 'position to term' rule for the sequence.

Example 6

The rule for a sequence is **multiply the term number by 4 and add 3**.
Find the first four terms of the sequence.

The first term is term number 1.   So first term $= \mathbf{1} \times 4 + 3 = 7$.

Similarly,   second term $= \mathbf{2} \times 4 + 3 = 11$
               third term $= \mathbf{3} \times 4 + 3 = 15$
               fourth term $= \mathbf{4} \times 4 + 3 = 19$

The first four terms are 7, 11, 15, 19.

> Notice that the differences between the terms are all 4.

Example 7

The rule for a sequence is **subtract 5 from the term number and
multiply by 6**. Find the ninth term.

The ninth term is term number 9.
So ninth term $= (\mathbf{9} - 5) \times 6$
$ = 4 \times 6$
$ = 24$

■ **The nth term of a sequence is an expression which gives you
the value of the term when you substitute the term number
into the expression.**

> $n = 1, 2, 3, \ldots$

■ **Your syllabus only includes the nth terms of sequences in
which the same number is added or subtracted to a term to
obtain the next term.**

> Such sequences are called **arithmetic** sequences.

Example 8

The nth term of a sequence is $3n + 5$. Find the first four terms.

substituting $n = 1$,   first term $= 3 \times \mathbf{1} + 5 = 3 + 5 = 8$
substituting $n = 2$, second term $= 3 \times \mathbf{2} + 5 = 6 + 5 = 11$
substituting $n = 3$,   third term $= 3 \times \mathbf{3} + 5 = 9 + 5 = 14$
substituting $n = 4$, fourth term $= 3 \times \mathbf{4} + 5 = 12 + 5 = 17$

The first four terms are 8, 11, 14, 17.

> The differences are all 3, the same as the coefficient of n in the nth term.

Example 9

The nth term of a sequence is $19 - 4n$. Find the first four terms.

substituting $n = 1$,   first term $= 19 - 4 \times \mathbf{1} = 19 - 4 = 15$
substituting $n = 2$, second term $= 19 - 4 \times \mathbf{2} = 19 - 8 = 11$
substituting $n = 3$,   third term $= 19 - 4 \times \mathbf{3} = 19 - 12 = 7$
substituting $n = 4$, fourth term $= 19 - 4 \times \mathbf{4} = 19 - 16 = 3$

The first four terms are 15, 11, 7, 3.

> The differences are all 4 and the terms are decreasing. The coefficient of n is −4.

Example 10

The nth term of a sequence is $7n - 23$. Find the tenth term.

substituting $n = 10$, tenth term $= 7 \times \mathbf{10} - 23$
$ = 70 - 23$
$ = 47$

Example 11

The first five terms of a sequence are 5, 11, 17, 23, 29.
Find an expression for the nth term of the sequence.

$$\begin{array}{ccccccccc} & 5 & & 11 & & 17 & & 23 & & 29 \\ \text{differences} & & 6 & & 6 & & 6 & & 6 \end{array}$$

The differences are all 6.
Example **8** suggest that the nth term will include $6n$ but an nth term of $6n$ gives the sequence 6, 12, 18, 24, 30, . . .
To obtain the required sequence, 1 must be subtracted from each term and so the nth term is $6n - 1$.

Example 12

The first five terms of a sequence are 8, 5, 2, −1, −4.
Find an expression for the nth term of the sequence.

The differences are all 3 and the terms are decreasing.
Example **9** suggests that the nth term will include $-3n$ but an nth term of $-3n$ gives the sequence $-3, -6, -9, -12, -15 \ldots$
To obtain the required sequence, 11 must be added to each term and so the nth term is $11 - 3n$.

Exercise 6B   Links (*2L*) 2L

1   For each of these rules, find
    (a) the first five terms in the sequence,
    (b) the twelfth term of the sequence.
        (i)   multiply the term number by 5 and subtract 2
        (ii) add 1 to the term number and multiply by 6
        (iii) multiply the term number by 8 and add 3
        (iv) multiply the term number by 3 and subtract from 16.

2   Write down an expression for the nth term of each of the
    sequences in question **1**.

3   For sequences with these nth terms, find
    (a) the first five terms in the sequence,
    (b) the twelfth term of the sequence.
        (i) $8n$ **(ii)** $2n + 1$ **(iii)** $5n - 4$
        (iv) $40 - 3n$ **(v)** $19 - 6n$

4   Here are the first five terms of some sequences.
    Find an expression for the nth term of each of the sequences:
    (a) 9, 18, 27, 36, 45, . . .   **(b)** 9, 14, 19, 24, 29, . . .
    (c) 12, 13, 14, 15, 16, . . .   **(d)** 21, 17, 13, 9, 5, . . .
    (e) 3, 13, 23, 33, 43, . . .   **(f)** 8, 7, 6, 5, 4, . . .
    (g) 23, 15, 7, −1, −9, . . .   **(h)** −12, −3, 6, 15, 24, . . .

5   Find an expression for the *n*th term of each of these
     sequences:
     (a) even numbers starting with 2
     (b) odd numbers starting with 1
     (c) multiples of 8 starting with 8
     (d) even numbers starting with 6
     (e) odd numbers starting with 9
     (f) multiples of 5 starting with 25.

6.3 Sequences of shapes

Teaching reference:
(*pp 25–27, section 2.9*)
pp 25–27, section 2.9

Example 13

Here are the first four shapes in a sequence of shapes made from matchsticks:

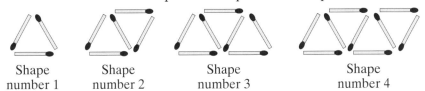

Shape	Shape	Shape	Shape
number 1	number 2	number 3	number 4

The table shows the number of matchsticks in each of these shapes:

Shape number (*n*)	1	2	3	4
Number of matchsticks	3	5	7	9

(a) Work out the number of matchsticks in shape number 5 and in
     shape number 6.
(b) Find an expression for the number of matchsticks in shape
     number *n*.

In other words, find the *n*th
term of the sequence
3, 5, 7, 9, . . .

(c) Find the number of matchsticks in shape number 20.
(d) Find the shape number of the shape with 57 matchsticks.

(a)   3   5   7   9
     differences   2   2   2

     In shape number 5, there are $9 + 2 = 11$ matchsticks.
     In shape number 6, there are $11 + 2 = 13$ matchsticks.
(b) The *n*th term will include $2n$ but an *n*th term of $2n$ gives the
     sequence 2, 4, 6, 8, 10, 12, . . .
     To obtain the required sequence, 1 must be added to each
     term and so the *n*th term is $2n + 1$.
(c) Substituting $n = 20$ in $2n + 1$ gives the number of matchsticks
     in shape number 20:
     number of matchsticks $= 2 \times 20 + 1 = 40 + 1 = 41$
(d) To find the shape number of the shape with 57 matchsticks,
     solve the equation $2n + 1 = 57$:

$$2n + 1 = 57$$
$$2n = 56 \quad (-1)$$
$$n = 28 \quad (\div 2)$$

     Shape number 28 has 57 matchsticks.

1   Here are the first four shapes in three sequences of shapes
    made from matchsticks:

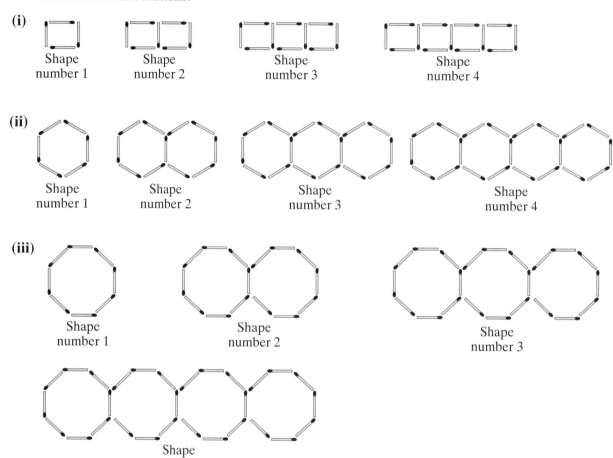

(i)

Shape
number 1

Shape
number 2

Shape
number 3

Shape
number 4

(ii)

Shape
number 1

Shape
number 2

Shape
number 3

Shape
number 4

(iii)

Shape
number 1

Shape
number 2

Shape
number 3

Shape
number 4

For each sequence:
  (a) work out the number of matchsticks in shape number 5
      and in shape number 6,
  (b) find an expression for the number of matchsticks in shape
      number n,
  (c) find the number of matchsticks in shape number 20,
  (d) find the shape number of the shape with 106 matchsticks.

2   (a) In question **1**, how is the coefficient of n in the expression
        for the number of matchsticks in shape number n related
        to the number of matchsticks in shape number 1?
        Explain why this is so.
    (b) Write down an expression for the number of matchsticks
        in shape number n when the matchsticks in shape number
        1 form a regular 12-sided polygon.

3 Here are four patterns of dots:

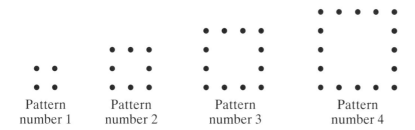

Pattern
number 1

Pattern
number 2

Pattern
number 3

Pattern
number 4

(a) Work out the number of dots in pattern number 5 and in pattern number 6.
(b) Find an expression for the number of dots in pattern number n.
(c) Find the number of dots in pattern number 31.
(d) Find the pattern number of the pattern with 92 dots.

4 Here are four patterns made with square tiles:

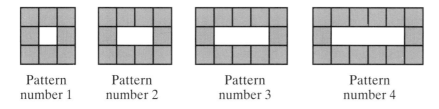

Pattern
number 1

Pattern
number 2

Pattern
number 3

Pattern
number 4

(a) Work out the number of tiles in pattern number 5 and in pattern number 6.
(b) Find an expression for the number of tiles in pattern number n.
(c) Find the number of tiles in pattern number 19.
(d) Find the pattern number of the pattern with 58 tiles.

5 Here are four patterns of dots:

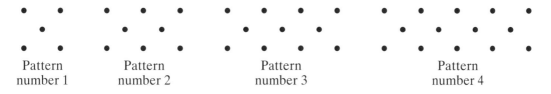

Pattern
number 1

Pattern
number 2

Pattern
number 3

Pattern
number 4

(a) Work out the number of dots in pattern number 5 and in pattern number 6.
(b) Find an expression for the number of dots in pattern number n.
(c) Find the number of dots in pattern number 23.
(d) Find the pattern number of the pattern with 80 dots.

6 Here are four patterns made with square tiles:

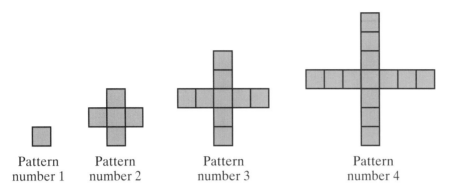

Pattern   Pattern   Pattern   Pattern
number 1   number 2   number 3   number 4

(a) Work out the number of tiles in pattern number 5 and in pattern number 6.
(b) Find an expression for the number of tiles in pattern number n.
(c) Find the number of tiles in pattern number 25.
(d) Find the pattern number of the pattern with 73 tiles.
(e) Find the pattern number of the largest pattern which can be made with 50 tiles.

7 Here are the first four shapes in a sequence of shapes made from matchsticks:

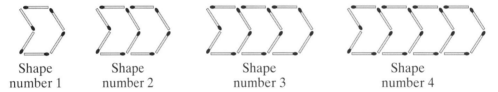

Shape   Shape   Shape   Shape
number 1   number 2   number 3   number 4

(a) Work out the number of matchsticks in shape number 5 and in shape number 6.
(b) Find an expression for the number of matchsticks in shape number n.
(c) Find the number of matchsticks in shape number 37.
(d) Find the shape number of the shape with 86 matchsticks.
(e) Find the shape number of the largest shape which can be made with 100 matchsticks.

8 Here are four patterns made with hexagonal tiles:

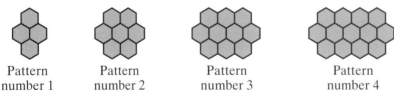

Pattern   Pattern   Pattern   Pattern
number 1   number 2   number 3   number 4

(a) Work out the number of tiles in pattern number 5 and in pattern number 6.
(b) Find an expression for the number of tiles in pattern number n.
(c) Find the number of tiles in pattern number 26.
(d) Find the pattern number of the pattern with 94 tiles.
(e) Find the pattern number of the largest pattern which can be made with 60 tiles.

Exercise 6D   Mixed questions

1 Find the next three terms in each of these sequences. You are told the first term and the term to term rule.
  (a) first term = 13; rule is **add 7**
  (b) first term = 3; rule is **multiply by 4**
  (c) first term = 5; rule is **multiply by 6 then subtract 1**
  (d) first term = 11; rule is **subtract 5 then multiply by 2**.

2 For each of these sequences
  (a) find the term to term rule for the sequence,
  (b) find the next two terms in the sequence.
    (i)   3, 11, 19, 27, 35, ...
    (ii) 8, 4, 2, 1, $\frac{1}{2}$, ...
    (iii) 20, 16, 12, 8, 4, ...
    (iv) 3, 7, 15, 31, 63, ...

3 For each of these position to term rules, find
  (a) the first five terms in the sequence,
  (b) the tenth term of the sequence,
  (c) an expression for the nth term of the sequence.
    (i)   **multiply the term number by 7 and add 5**
    (ii) **multiply the term number by 9 and subtract 8**
    (iii) **multiply the term number by 5 and subtract from 20**.

4 For sequences with these nth terms, find
  (a) the first five terms in the sequence,
  (b) the twentieth term of the sequence.
    (i) $9n$
    (ii) $3n + 7$
    (iii) $5n - 11$
    (iv) $28 - 7n$
    (v) $8 - 9n$

5 Here are the first five terms of some sequences.
  Find an expression for the nth term of each of the sequences.
  (a) 7, 13, 19, 25, 31, ...
  (b) 23, 20, 17, 14, 11, ...
  (c) 0, 7, 14, 21, 28, ...
  (d) 5, −4, −13, −22, −31, ...

6 The nth term of a sequence is $8n - 3$. A term of the sequence is 101. Find the term number of 101.

7 The nth term of a sequence is $3 - 8n$. A term of the sequence is −141. Find the term number of −141.

8 47 is a term of the sequence 2, 11, 20, 29, 38, ...
  Find the term number of 47.

9 −94 is a term of the sequence 8, 5, 2, −1, −4, ...
  Find the term number of −94.

10 Here are the first four shapes in a sequence of shapes made from matchsticks:

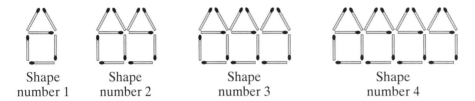

| Shape number 1 | Shape number 2 | Shape number 3 | Shape number 4 |

(a) Work out the number of matchsticks in shape number 5 and in shape number 6.

(b) Find an expression for the number of matchsticks in shape number n.

(c) Find the number of matchsticks in shape number 18.

(d) Find the shape number of the shape with 66 matchsticks.

(e) Find the shape number of the largest shape which can be made with 100 matchsticks.

11 Here are four patterns made with octagonal tiles and square tiles:

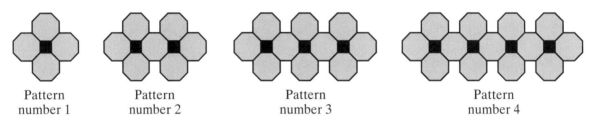

| Pattern number 1 | Pattern number 2 | Pattern number 3 | Pattern number 4 |

(a) Work out the *total* number of tiles in pattern number 5 and in pattern number 6.

(b) Find an expression for the number of *octagonal* tiles in pattern number n.

(c) Find an expression for the *total* number of tiles in pattern number n.

(d) Find the number of octagonal tiles in pattern number 10.

(e) Find the total number of tiles in pattern number 17.

(f) Find the number of octagonal tiles in a pattern with 9 square tiles.

(g) Find the total number of tiles in a pattern with 55 octagonal tiles.

Summary of key points

- A sequence is a succession of numbers formed according to a rule.

- The numbers in a sequence are called the *terms* of the sequence.

- One type of rule for a sequence tells you what to do to each term to obtain the next term in the sequence.

  This is called a 'term to term' rule for the sequence.

- To find the rule for a sequence, it is often helpful to find the differences between consecutive terms.

- Another type of rule for a sequence tells you what to do to the term number to obtain that term in the sequence.

- The nth term of a sequence is an expression which gives you the value of the term when you substitute the term number into the expression.

- Your syllabus only includes the nth terms of sequences in which the same number is added or subtracted to a term to obtain the next term.

This is called a 'position to term' rule for the sequence.

7 Properties of shapes

7.1 Polygons

■   **A polygon is a 2-D shape with any number of sides.**

This table shows the special names used for polygons depending on the number of sides:

Number of sides	Name of polygon
3	triangle
4	quadrilateral
5	pentagon
6	hexagon
7	heptagon
8	octagon
9	nonagon
10	decagon

■   **A polygon is regular if all its sides and all its angles are equal.**

■   **The point where two sides meet is called a *corner* or *vertex*. The plural of vertex is vertices.**

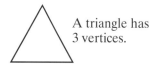
A triangle has 3 vertices.

■   **The angle at a vertex is a measure of the turn between two sides that meet there. Angles are usually measured in degrees.**

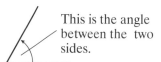
This is the angle between the two sides.

Exercise 7A   Links (4A) 4A

Write down the names of these polygons:

1
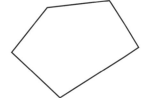

2
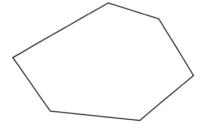

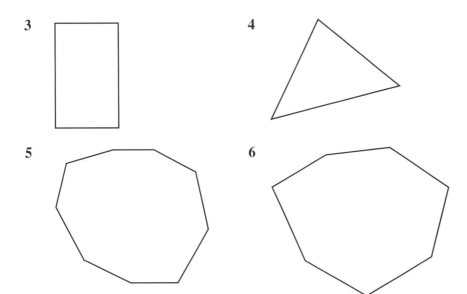

3

4

5

6

7.2 Properties of triangles

■ **A triangle is a polygon which has 3 sides.**

■ **The interior angles of a triangle add up to 180°.**

3 sides

3 angles add up
to 180°

You need to recognize these special types of triangle:

Name	Shape	Properties
Scalene triangle		no sides equal no angles equal
Isosceles triangle		2 sides equal 2 angles equal
Equilateral triangle	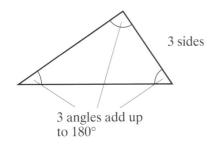	3 sides equal 3 angles equal and 60°

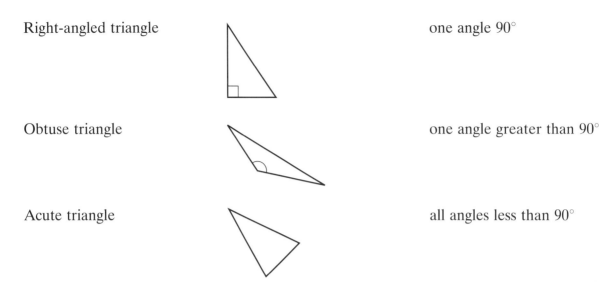

Right-angled triangle   one angle 90°

Obtuse triangle   one angle greater than 90°

Acute triangle   all angles less than 90°

(Note: scalene and isosceles triangles can be acute or obtuse.
Equilateral triangles are always acute.)

Exercise 7B   Links (4A) 4A

Write down the names of these special types of triangle.
The first one is done for you.

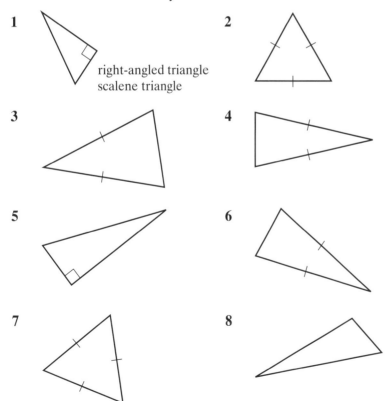

1   right-angled triangle
scalene triangle

2

3

4

5

6

7

8

7.3 Properties of quadrilaterals

■   A quadrilateral is a polygon which has 4 sides.

■   The interior angles of a quadrilateral add up to 360°.

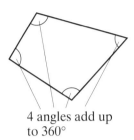

4 angles add up
to 360°

You need to recognize these special types of quadrilateral:

Name	Shape	Properties
Trapezium		1 pair of parallel sides
Parallelogram		2 pairs of parallel sides opposite sides equal opposite angles equal diagonals bisect each other
Rhombus		2 pairs of parallel sides opposite angles equal all sides equal diagonals bisect each other at right angles diagonals bisect the angles at the vertices
Rectangle		2 pairs of parallel sides all angles are 90° opposite sides are equal diagonals are equal and bisect each other
Square		all sides equal all angles 90° opposite sides parallel diagonals are equal and bisect each other at right angles

Kite

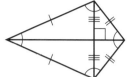

two pairs of adjacent sides equal
one pair of opposite angles equal
diagonals cross at right angles
one diagonal bisected by the other diagonal

Arrowhead

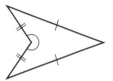

two pairs of adjacent sides equal
one angle bigger than 180°

Exercise 7C   **Links (4A) 4A**

Write down the names of these special types of quadrilateral.
The first one is done for you.

1

trapezium

2

3

4
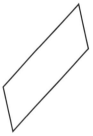

5
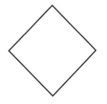

6
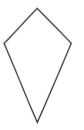

7
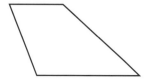

8

9 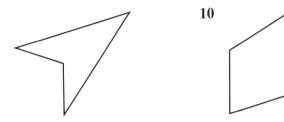 **10**

11 Write down the names of all quadrilaterals with
  (a) all angles 90°
  (b) opposite sides parallel
  (c) one angle greater than 180°
  (d) diagonals that bisect each other
  (e) two pairs of adjacent sides equal.

12 Write down the names of the special quadrilaterals below and
  show their properties on the diagrams:
  (a) 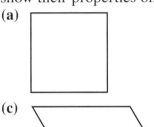   **(b)**

  (c) 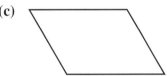   **(d)**

7.4 Properties of circles

Teaching reference:
(*pp 131–133, section 10.4*)
pp 163–166, section 10.4

■ **A circle is the shape enclosed by a curve which is everywhere
the same distance from the centre.**

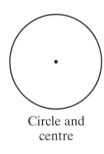

Circle and
centre

Circle and
radius

Circle and
diameter

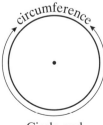

Circle and
circumference

Circle and
sector

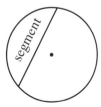

Circle and
segment

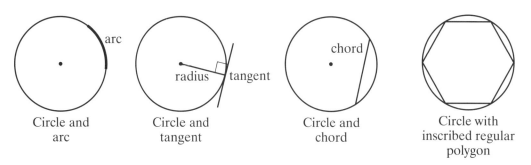

Circle and arc | Circle and tangent | Circle and chord | Circle with inscribed regular polygon

■ The circumference of a circle is the distance measured around the curve which makes the circle.

■ A chord is a straight line drawn across a circle.

■ A tangent to a circle touches the circle at one point only. The radius is at 90° to the tangent.

■ Inscribed regular polygons can be constructed by equal division of a circle.

| Exercise 7D | Links (*10D*) 10D |

1 Draw a diagram to show radius, diameter and circumference of a circle.
2 Draw a diagram to show an arc, circumference and tangent.
3 Draw a diagram to show a chord, sector and segment.

Summary of key points

■ A polygon is a 2-D shape with any number of sides.

■ A polygon is regular if all its sides and all its angles are equal.

■ The point where two sides meet is called a *corner* or *vertex*. The plural of vertex is vertices.

■ The angle at a vertex is a measure of the turn between two sides that meet there. Angles are usually measured in degrees.

■ A triangle is a polygon which has 3 sides.

■ The interior angles of a triangle add up to 180°.

■ A quadrilateral is a polygon which has 4 sides.

■ The interior angles of a quadrilateral add up to 360°.

■ The circumference of a circle is the distance measured around the curve which makes the circle.

■ A chord is a straight line drawn across a circle.

■ A tangent to a circle touches the circle at one point only. The radius is at 90° to the tangent.

■ Inscribed regular polygons can be constructed by equal division of a circle.

8 Symmetry and transformations

8.1 Line symmetry and rotational symmetry

■ A 2-D shape has a line of symmetry if the line divides the shape into two halves and one half is the mirror image of the other half.

Example 1

Copy this shape and draw with dotted lines all the lines of symmetry.

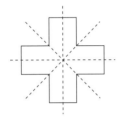

When the shape is folded on the dotted lines one half fits exactly on top of the other. Tracing paper will help you check.

Example 2

Complete this drawing so that the dotted line is the axis of symmetry:

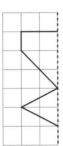

Mark the mirror images of the vertices then join up the points:

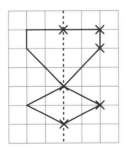

■ A 2-D shape has rotational symmetry if it fits onto itself two or more times in one turn.

■ The order of rotational symmetry is the number of times a shape fits onto itself in one turn.

Example 3

Write down the order of rotational symmetry of this shape:

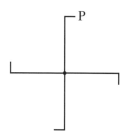

This shape will fit onto itself 4 times when rotated about its centre through 360°:

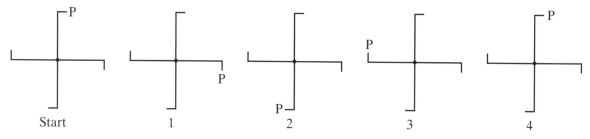

| Start | 1 | 2 | 3 | 4 |

It has rotational symmetry of order 4.

| **Exercise 8A** | **Links (*4C*) 4C** |

Tracing paper will help you to find the symmetry in this Exercise.

1   Copy these shapes and draw with dotted lines any lines of symmetry that they might have:

(a)
(b)

(c)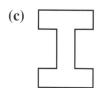
(d)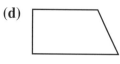

(e)
(f)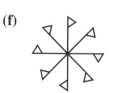

2   Write down the order of rotational symmetry for each shape in question **1**.

3 Copy and complete each drawing so that the dotted line is an axis of symmetry:

(a)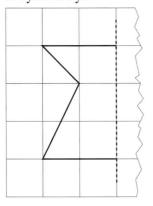

(b)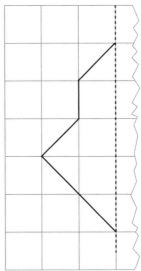

(c)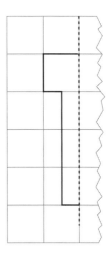

(d)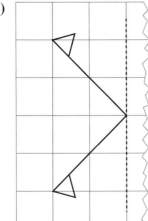

(e)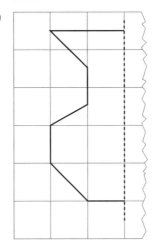

(f)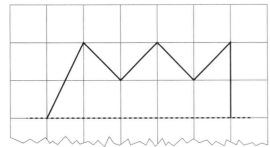

4 Draw a shape that has rotational symmetry of order

(a) 2   **(b)** 5   **(c)** 10   **(d)** none.

8.2 **Planes of symmetry**

Teaching reference:
(*pp 47–50, section 4.4*)
pp 47–50, section 4.4

■ **A 3-D shape has a plane of symmetry if the plane divides the shape into two halves and one half is the mirror image of the other half.**

Example 4

Copy this 3-D shape and draw a plane of symmetry:

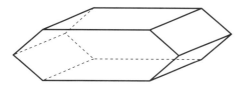

Here is a plane of symmetry:

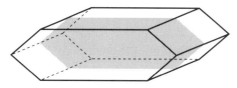

Exercise 8B   **Links (4D) 4D**

1   Draw 2 copies of each of these 3-D shapes. On each of them draw a plane of symmetry.

(a) 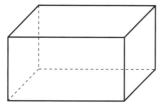   (b)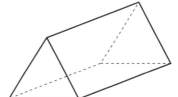

(c) 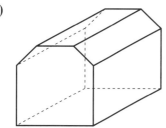   (d)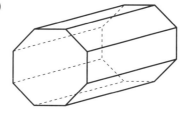

2   Copy, and draw the specified number of planes of symmetry for each shape:

(a) 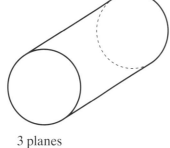   (b)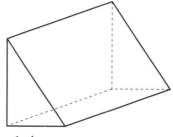

3 planes   1 plane

8.3 Reflections

■ **A reflection in a line produces a mirror image.**

■ **To describe a reflection fully you need to give the equation of the line of reflection.**

Teaching reference:
(*pp 336–339, sections 23.2, 23.3*)
pp 370–373, section 23.2

Example 5

Reflect the shape in the mirror line:

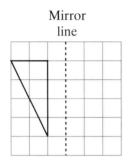

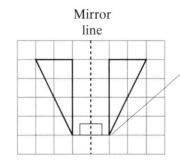

Note:
Each vertex is exactly the same distance from the mirror line at a right angle to it.

Example 6

Describe fully the single transformation which maps shape **A** onto shape **B**:

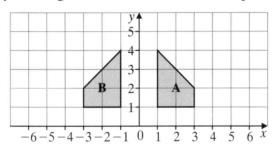

A reflection in the *y*-axis (or the line $x = 0$).

Example 7

Reflect **A** in the line $y = 0$; call the shape **B**.

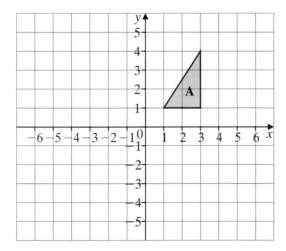

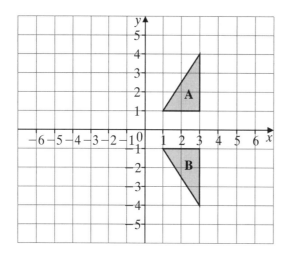

Remember: tracing paper will help you.

Exercise 8C   Links (*23C*) 23B

You need tracing paper and squared paper.

1   Copy these diagrams. Reflect each shape in the mirror line M.

(a)   M

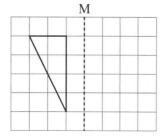

(b)   M

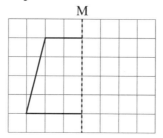

(c)   M

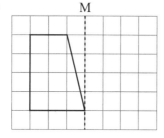

(d)   M

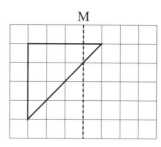

(e)   M

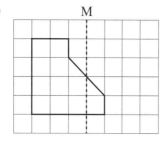

(f)

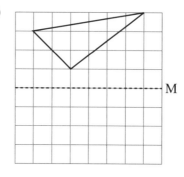

2   Describe fully the single transformation which maps
   (a) **A** onto **B**   **(b)** **B** onto **C**   **(c)** **C** onto **D**.

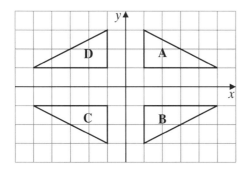

3   Draw a separate diagram for each shape.
   Reflect each shape in the lines $x = 0$ and $y = 0$.
   Label them **P** and **Q** respectively.

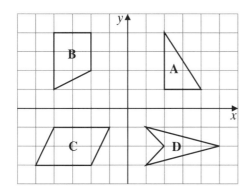

8.4 Rotations

Teaching reference:
(*pp 339–343, section 23.3*)
pp 373–377, section 23.3

■   **A rotation turns a shape through an angle about a fixed point.**

■   **To describe a rotation fully you need to give the**
   • **centre of rotation**
   • **angle of turn**
   • **direction of turn.**

Example 8

Rotate the shape a quarter turn anticlockwise about point P.

Trace the shape and rotate it 90° anticlockwise to find the new position:

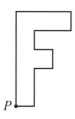
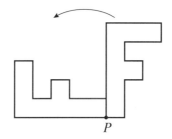

Example 9

On the grid rotate the shape **A** a half turn about the origin.
Call the new shape **B**.

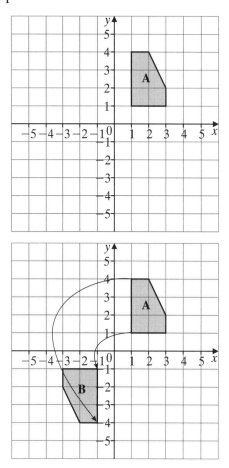

Example 10

Describe fully the transformation which maps **P** onto **Q**:

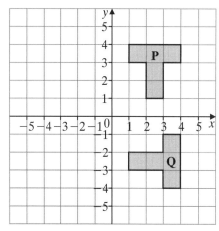

The transformation is a rotation described by: a clockwise quarter
turn, centre the origin.

Note: a clockwise quarter
turn is the same as a turn
through −90°, centre the
origin.

Exercise 8D **Links** (*23C, 23D, 23E*) 23C, 23D, 23E

You may find tracing paper useful in this exercise.

1 Copy the shapes. Rotate each shape a $\frac{1}{2}$ turn and a $\frac{1}{4}$ turn anticlockwise about the point *P*.

(a)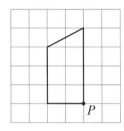

(b)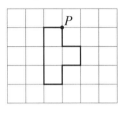

(c)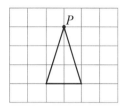

2 Copy this shape. Draw the image
of the shape after rotations
about point *P* of
(a) 60°
(b) 150°
(c) 210°

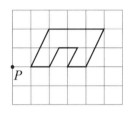

Remember: a positive angle
is anticlockwise.

3 Draw separate coordinate grids with *x*- and *y*-axes from −6 to
+6. On each of the four grids copy one of shapes **A**, **B**, **C**
and **D**. Draw the image of each shape after
(a) a quarter turn of 90° about (0, 0)
(b) a half turn about (0, 0)
(c) a −60° turn about (0, 0).

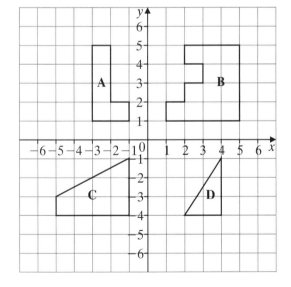

4   Shape **P** has been rotated 3 times. Describe fully the rotation
     which takes **P** to each of positions **A**, **B**, and **C**.

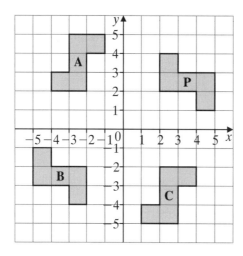

8.5 Translations

Teaching reference:
(pp 333–336, section 23.1)
pp 367–370, section 23.1

■   **A translation moves every point on a shape the same distance
     in the same direction.**

■   **To describe a translation fully you need to give the distance
     moved and the direction of movement. You can do this by
     writing down the vector of the translation.**

Example 11

Translate the shape **P** by the translation vector $\begin{pmatrix} 3 \\ 2 \end{pmatrix}$.

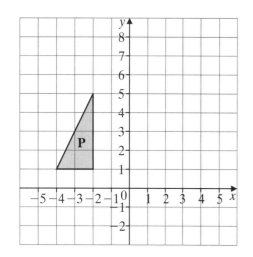

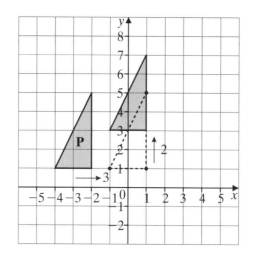

Example 12

Describe the transformation which has mapped **P** onto **Q**:

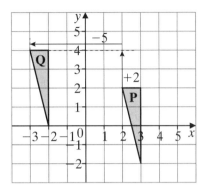

The translation is -5 and $+2$, written as translation $\begin{pmatrix} -5 \\ 2 \end{pmatrix}$.

Exercise 8E   Links (*23A*) 23A

1   Copy this shape onto squared paper. Translate the shape by
    the following translation vectors:

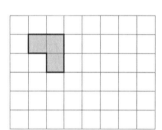

   (a) $\begin{pmatrix} 1 \\ 2 \end{pmatrix}$; call it **A**   (b) $\begin{pmatrix} 3 \\ 5 \end{pmatrix}$; call it **B**

   (c) $\begin{pmatrix} -2 \\ 3 \end{pmatrix}$; call it **C**   (d) $\begin{pmatrix} 2 \\ -3 \end{pmatrix}$; call it **D**

   (e) $\begin{pmatrix} -2 \\ -5 \end{pmatrix}$; call it **E**.

2   The shape **P** has been translated into four different positions;
    R, S, T, V. Write down the translation vector for each
    translation.

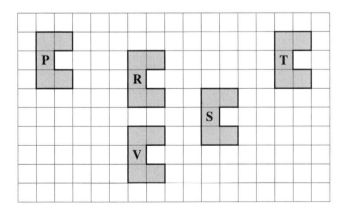

3 Describe the transformation which maps **T** onto each shape **A**, **B**, **C** and **D**:

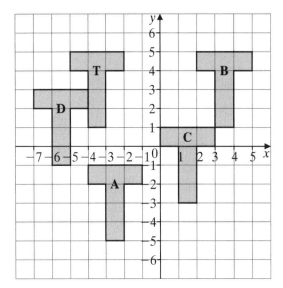

4 Transform shape **P** by the translation vectors

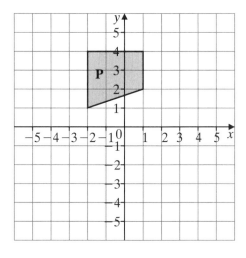

(a) $\begin{pmatrix} -1 \\ -3 \end{pmatrix}$; call it **A**

(b) $\begin{pmatrix} 3 \\ -4 \end{pmatrix}$; call it **B**

(c) $\begin{pmatrix} 4 \\ 2 \end{pmatrix}$; call it **C**

(d) $\begin{pmatrix} -1 \\ 0 \end{pmatrix}$; call it **D**.

Summary of key points

- A 2-D shape has a line of symmetry if the line divides the shape into two halves and one half is the mirror image of the other half.

- A 2-D shape has rotational symmetry if it fits onto itself two or more times in one turn.

- The order of rotational symmetry is the number of times a shape fits onto itself in one turn.

- A 3-D shape has a plane of symmetry if the plane divides the shape into two halves and one half is the mirror image of the other half.

- A reflection in a line produces a mirror image.
- To describe a reflection fully you need to give the equation of the line of reflection.
- A rotation turns a shape through an angle about a fixed point.
- To describe a rotation fully you need to give the
  - centre of rotation
  - angle of turn
  - direction of turn.
- A translation moves every point on a shape the same distance in the same direction.
- To describe a translation fully you need to give the distance moved and the direction of movement. You can do this by writing down the vector of translation.

9 Angles, constructions and bearings

9.1 Construction

Teaching reference:
(*pp 385–387, section 26.1*)
pp 425–428, section 26.1

Example 1

Construct an accurate diagram for the sketch.

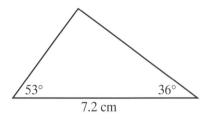

Draw the length first.

7.2 cm

Use a protractor to mark the angles at each end.

53°   36°
7.2 cm

Complete the triangle.

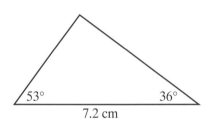

Exercise 9A   Links (*5I, 26A*) 5I, 26A

1   Measure these lines. Give your answers in both millimetres and centimetres.

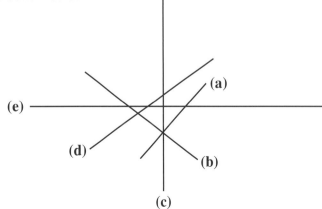

2 Draw, to the nearest mm, lines of length
(a) 3.6 cm (b) 54 mm (c) 4.9 cm (d) 73 mm (e) 6.2 cm

3 Construct triangle *ABC* with
(a) angle $B = 35°$, angle $C = 61°$, $BC = 5$ cm
(b) angle $A = 81°$, angle $C = 50°$, $AC = 3.2$ cm
(c) angle $B = 44°$, angle $A = 121°$, $AB = 4$ cm
(d) angle $A = 117°$, angle $C = 32°$, $AC = 36$ mm.
In each case measure and write down the lengths of the other sides.

4 Construct accurate figures for the diagrams shown:
(a) 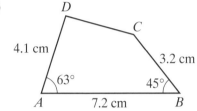   (b)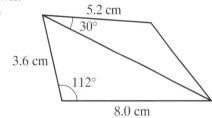

Measure length *DC* and angle *C*.

9.2 Nets

Teaching reference:
(*pp 50–51, section 4.5*)
pp 50–51, section 4.5

Example 2
Draw the net of a cube.

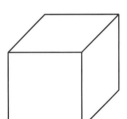

Imagine the cube opened up.

flattening out to

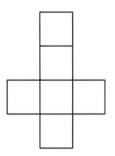

This is the net which could be used to construct a cube.

Exercise 9B   Links (*4E*) 4E

1   Construct an accurate net for this cuboid.

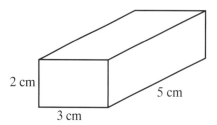

2   Sketch a net for this prism:

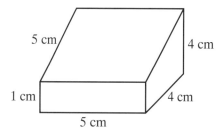

3   Draw an accurate net to construct a regular tetrahedron.

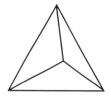

> In a regular tetrahedron all faces are equilateral triangles.

4   What shape will this net make? Draw a sketch of the shape.

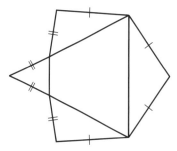

5   Could this be the net of a solid?
    Give reasons for your answer.

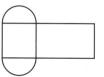

6   Which of these nets would make a square-based pyramid?

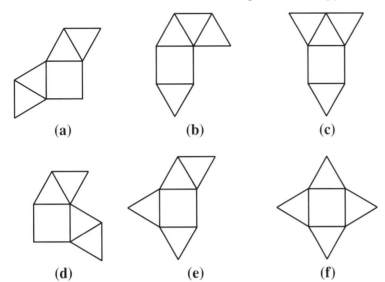

(a)   **(b)**   **(c)**

(d)   **(e)**   **(f)**

9.3 Parallel lines, alternate and corresponding angles

Teaching reference:
(*pp 129–131, section 10.3*)
pp 159–162, section 10.3

■   Angles on a straight line add up to 180°.

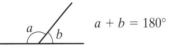 $a + b = 180°$

■   Angles in a triangle add up to 180°.
■   The exterior angle of a triangle is equal to the sum of the interior angles at the other two vertices.

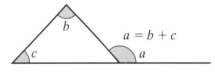 $a = b + c$

■   Vertically opposite angles are equal.

■   Base angles of an isosceles triangle are equal.
■   A straight line crossing parallel lines creates corresponding angles.
    Corresponding angles are equal.

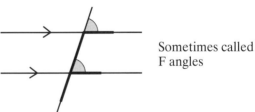   Sometimes called F angles

■   A straight line crossing parallel lines creates alternate angles.
    Alternate angles are equal.

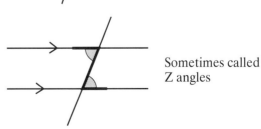   Sometimes called Z angles

Example 3

In the diagram, *ABE* is isosceles with *EA* = *EB*.
Work out, with reasons, the size of the acute angle at *C*.

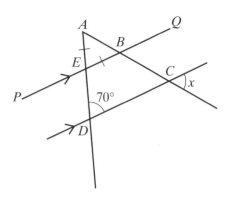

angle *AEB* = 70°   corresponding angles
angle *EAB* = angle *EBA*   isosceles triangle
angle *EAB* + angle *EBA* = 110°   angles of a triangle add up to 180°
angle *EBA* = 55°
angle *QBC* = 55°   vertically opposite angles
x = 55°   corresponding angles

Exercise 9C   Links (*10C*) 10C

1   Find the marked angles:

(a) 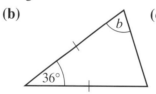   **(b)** 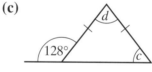   **(c)** 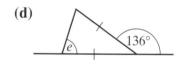   **(d)**

2   Work out the value of the letter:

(a) 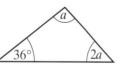   **(b)** 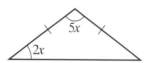   **(c)**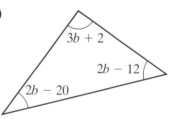

(d) 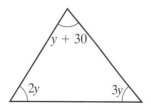   **(e)**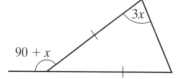

3   Give the size of *a*.
Give a reason for your answer.

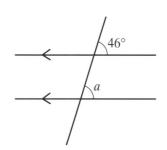

4   Give the size of *b*.
Give a reason for your answer.

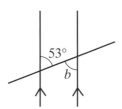

In each of the following questions, work out the size of the marked angle(s). You must give reason(s).

5

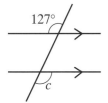

6

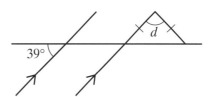

7

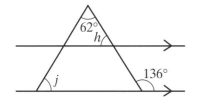

8

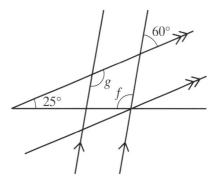

9

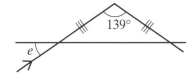

10

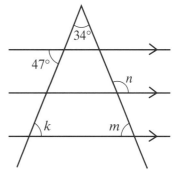

9.4 Interior and exterior angles of polygons

Teaching reference:
(*pp 126–128, section 10.2*)
pp 156–158, section 10.2

- The sum of the exterior angles of any polygon is 360°.
- At each vertex of a polygon the sum of the interior angle and exterior angle is 180°.
- The sum of the interior angles of a polygon with *n* sides is (*n* − 2) × 180°.

Example 4

A regular polygon has interior angles of 156°.
How many sides has it got?

The exterior angles must be 180 − 156 = 24°.

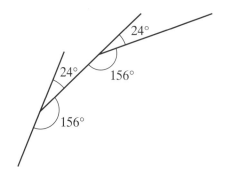

The sum of the exterior angles is always 360°.
So there must be 360/24 = 15 exterior angles.
It must be a 15-sided polygon.

Exercise 9D	Links (*10B*) 10B

1 A regular nonagon has 9 sides.
   Work out the size of
   (a) an exterior angle   **(b)** an interior angle.
   Hence work out the sum of the interior angles of a nonagon.

2 A regular polygon has interior angles of 165°.
   How many sides has it got?

3 The angle sum of a regular polygon is 1440°.
   How many sides has it got?

4 Work out the size of the missing angles in these quadrilaterals:
   (a)   **(b)**   **(c)**

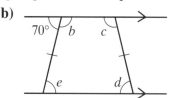
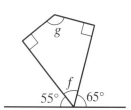

5 Use this diagram to show that the angles of a triangle add up to 180°:

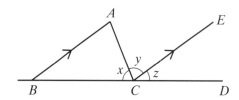

A tessellation is an arrangement of shapes that fills a flat area
without overlapping or leaving any gaps.

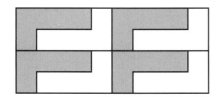 or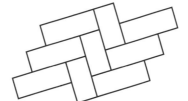

6 Show how a kite will tessellate.

7 Investigate the statement 'All quadrilaterals will tessellate
using a combination of half turns and transformations'.

Exercise 9E   Mixed questions

1 Construct as accurately as possible the diagrams shown:

(a) 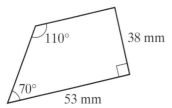   **(b)**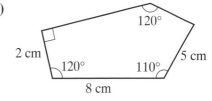

Write down the lengths of the unmarked sides.

2 Explain why this cannot be the net of a solid.

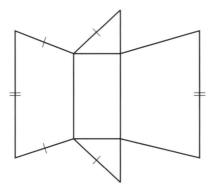

3 Which of these nets could possibly produce the dice shown?

 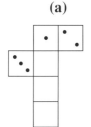 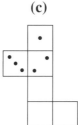 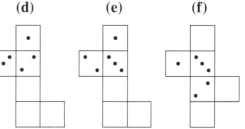

4 In each of these diagrams work out the size of the marked angles. You must also give reasons.

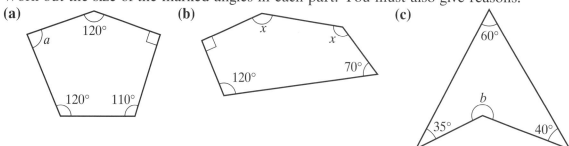

(a)   **(b)**   **(c)**

5 The exterior angle of a regular polygon is $9°$.
How many sides has it got?
What is the sum of its interior angles?

6 Work out the size of the marked angles in each part. You must also give reasons.

(a)   **(b)**   **(c)**

9.5 Bearings

■ **A three-figure bearing gives a direction in degrees. It is an angle measured clockwise from the North.**

Example 5

Give the three-figure bearing of
(i) A from B
(ii) C from D.

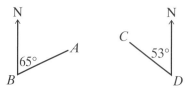

(i) The angle is $65°$.
As this is measured clockwise from North the bearing is $065°$.
(ii) The angle is $53°$ measured anticlockwise from North. This is
$360° - 53° = 307°$ measured clockwise.
The bearing is $307°$.

Example 6

The bearing of Witney from Oxford is 283°.
What is the bearing of Oxford from Witney?

To face Oxford from Witney you have to do a half turn.
This is a change of direction of 180°.

In this case, you subtract 180°.
The bearing of Oxford from Witney is 283° − 180° = 103°.

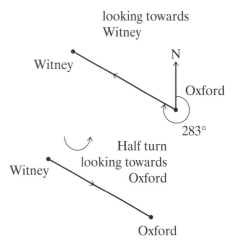

Exercise 9F

1

Using the map of South Wales find the bearing of
(a) Brecon from Swansea
(b) Lampeter from Pembroke
(c) Cardigan from Aberystwyth
(d) St Davids from Cardigan
(e) Swansea from Cardiff
(f) Cardigan from Monmouth
(g) Lampeter from Newtown
(h) Swansea from Aberystwyth

2 *A*, *B* and *C* are three towns. The bearing of *B* from *A* is 070°. The bearing of *B* from *C* is 125°. The bearing of *C* from *A* is 330°. Draw a sketch to show the relative position of the towns.

3 The bearing of Charlbury from Oxford is 310°. What is the bearing of Oxford from Charlbury?

4 The bearing of Bicester from Woodstock is 055°. What is the bearing of Woodstock from Bicester?

5 Measure and write down the bearing of
   (a) *B* from *C*
   (b) *A* from *C*
   (c) *C* from *B*
   (d) *B* from *A*

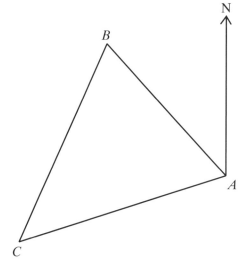

Summary of key points

■   **Angles on a straight line add up to 180°.**

■   **Angles in a triangle add up to 180°.**

■   **Vertically opposite angles are equal.**

■   **Base angles of an isosceles triangle are equal.**

■   **Corresponding angles are equal.**

■   **Alternate angles are equal.**

■   **The sum of the exterior angles of any polygon is 360°.**

■   **At each vertex of a polygon the sum of the interior angle and exterior angle is 180°.**

■   **The sum of the interior angles of a polygon with n sides is $(n-2) \times 180°$.**

■   **A three-figure bearing gives a direction in degrees. It is an angle measured clockwise from the North.**

10 Handling data

10.1 Collecting data

Teaching reference:
(*pp 98–108, sections 8.1–8.8*)
pp 100–115, sections 8.1–8.10

- Data collected through experiments, surveys, questionnaires, etc. is called *primary data*.

- Data extracted from published sources is called *secondary data*.

- Two-way tables can be used for discrete, continuous and grouped data.

- When data is collected all attempts to eliminate bias should be made.

- There are occasions when you need to make decisions about missing data.

Example 1

Jon is collecting data on the types of sport people watch on TV.
In his questionnaire he asks the question

'You like watching sport on TV, don't you?'

(a) Explain why the above question is a poor one.
(b) Write the first two good questions you believe Jon could ask.

(a) The question is a poor one because it is leading. It actually tells people, or at least suggests to them that they *do* like watching sport on TV.
(b) The first question should be something like

Do you enjoy watching sport on TV?   Yes   No   (Delete as appropriate)

If your answer to the above question is 'Yes', please answer the next question:

Place a tick in the three boxes next to your 3 favourite sports to watch on TV.

Snooker   ☐

Rugby   ☐

Tennis   ☐

Football   ☐

Horse racing   ☐

Cricket   ☐

Other   ☐

Example 2

This table is an extract from a motor car dealer's advertisement.

(a) Write down the make of car which has a price under £2000.
(b) What is the make of the oldest car in this list?
(c) Write down the registration and age of the car that has completed the greatest mileage.

Price	Make	Age	Registration	Mileage
£12 500	Rover	1	Y	1 200
£6 500	Ford	3	R	18 000
£2 500	Peugeot	7	M	92 000
£1 995	Seat	6	K	78 000
£9 800	Vauxhall	2	V	11 000
£3 995	Saab	8	L	63 000
£5 495	Toyota	4	R	48 000
£9 500	Ford	1	X	12 000

(a) Seat.
(b) The oldest car is a Saab.
(c) Registration M, age 7.

Example 3

A set of 30 times in seconds is recorded, but the last result is missing.

```
12.8   10.0    4.3   16.1    5.6   18.2   14.3   11.6   22.0   18.3
22.1    5.9   13.5    3.2   11.5   10.7   15.3    4.2    7.8    8.8
 6.5   17.0    7.4   12.9   13.2   11.7   23.0   16.4   15.3
```

Complete the frequency table below:

Time (t) seconds	Tally	Frequency
$0 < t \leqslant 5$		
$5 < t \leqslant 10$		
$10 < t \leqslant 15$		
$15 < t \leqslant 20$		
$20 < t \leqslant 25$		

What could be done about the missing result?

Time (t) seconds	Tally	Frequency
$0 < t \leqslant 5$	|||	3
$5 < t \leqslant 10$	卌 ||	7
$10 < t \leqslant 15$	卌 ||||	9
$15 < t \leqslant 20$	卌 ||	7
$20 < t \leqslant 25$	|||	3

If 30 results are needed then you need to record one more result. But if the 30 is not an imperative for the outcome of the survey then proceed with 29 results.

Example 4

Copy and complete this two-way table for the types of holiday chosen by 100 people.

	Beach	Lakes and Mountains	Cities	Totals
Men	28		10	53
Women		16	15	
Totals				100

The number of Lakes and Mountains holidays chosen by men must be

   53 (the total number of men) $- (28 + 10) = 53 - 38 = 15$

The total number of women must be

   100 (the total number of people) $- 53$ (the number of men) $= 100 - 53 = 47$

The total number of Beach holidays chosen by women will then be

   47 (the total number of women) $- (16 + 15) = 47 - 31 = 16$

This information now gives the following:
The total for Beach holidays is $28 + 16 = 44$
The total for Lakes and Mountains is $15 + 16 = 31$
The total for Cities is $10 + 15 = 25$

So the completed table is:

	Beach	Lakes and Mountains	Cities	Totals
Men	28	**15**	10	53
Women	**16**	16	15	**47**
Totals	**44**	**31**	**25**	100

Exercise 10A   Links (*8A–8G*) 8A–8L

1   George and Asif are carrying out a survey on the food students eat in the college canteen. George wrote the question

      'Which foods do you eat?'

    Asif comments that the question is too vague.

    Write down three ways in which the question could be improved.

2   Thirty-two people order drinks in a cafe one evening.
    Here is a list of the drinks they order:

Coffee	Coke	Lemon	Tea	Coffee	Coffee	Tea	Coffee
Tea	Lemon	Coffee	Coke	Tea	Orange	Tea	Lemon
Coke	Coke	Coffee	Orange	Coke	Coffee	Lemon	Coke
Coffee	Tea	Orange	Coke	Milk	Coffee	Coffee	Tea

    Design and complete a tally chart and frequency table for this information.

3 Sammi wishes to work out her average mark for 10 Science homeworks. When she checks her book she can only find nine marks:

    6,   6,   8,   7,   9,   5,   4,   8,   7

Explain the possible alternative way she can work out her average mark for the Science homeworks.

4 Jenny and Reyhana are collecting information about the type of meal bought in the works canteen.
Design a suitable data capture sheet they could use.

5 Karen conducts a survey into the ages of people visiting a supermarket one lunchtime. She has the following list of 60 ages:

32	41	27	16	22	23	13	8	11	28	37	54	64	12	70
44	18	19	22	30	15	43	17	21	27	34	35	36	42	19
73	65	28	17	16	45	51	27	14	43	12	36	11	9	10
55	67	18	23	24	16	10	43	44	52	56	18	17	26	58

Design and complete a grouped frequency table which records these ages in five-yearly intervals. Start with the class interval

    $0 < \text{age} \leqslant 5$

6 A group of 80 students were asked to provide information about the number of videos and DVDs they owned. Some of the results are provided in the two-way table below:

	Videos	DVDs	Totals
Boys	21		38
Girls		27	
Totals			80

Complete the two-way table.

Summary of key points

- Data collected through experiments, surveys, questionnaires, etc. is called *primary data*.
- Data extracted from published sources is called *secondary data*.
- Two-way tables can be used for discrete, continuous and grouped data.
- When data is collected all attempts to eliminate bias should be made.
- There are occasions when you need to make decisions about missing data or rogue values.

11 Probability

Probability is used to predict the chance of things, called events, happening in the future.

11.1 Probability

Teaching reference:
(*pp 28–38, sections 3.1–3.4*)
pp 28–38, sections 3.1–3.4

■ **Probability is measured on a scale from 0 to 1. You must write a probability as a fraction, a decimal or a percentage.**

■ **The estimated probability of an event or experiment**

$$= \frac{\textbf{number of successful trials}}{\textbf{total number of trials}}$$

This is also called the *relative frequency*.

■ **The calculated probability of an event happening**

$$= \frac{\textbf{number of successful outcomes}}{\textbf{total number of possible outcomes}}$$

■ **When one outcome prevents another outcome from happening the outcomes are mutually exclusive. The probabilities of all the possible mutually exclusive outcomes add up to 1.**

When you toss a coin the outcomes Heads and Tails are mutually exclusive.

■ **For two events A and B which are mutually exclusive**
P(A or B) = P(A) + P(B)
This is called the OR rule.

■ **If the probability of an event happening is *p* then the probability of the event not happening is $1 - p$.**

■ **If there are *n* mutually exclusive outcomes, all equally likely,**

the probability of one outcome happening is $\frac{1}{n}$.

■ **If there are *n* mutually exclusive outcomes and *a* of these are deemed successful then the probability of a successful**

outcome is $\frac{a}{n}$.

■ **When the outcome of one event does not affect the outcome of another event, they are called *independent* events.**

When you toss a coin and roll a dice together the events are independent; one does not affect the other.

Example 1

Joan has a bag of 15 chocolates.
8 chocolates are plain, 4 are milk and the remaining 3 are white.

Joan puts her hand in the bag and chooses a chocolate at random.
Each chocolate has an equal chance of being selected.

Work out the probability of Joan selecting a chocolate which is
(a) white
(b) either milk or white
(c) not milk
(d) a sugared almond.

(a) There are 3 white chocolates out of a total of 15. So the
probability of a white chocolate being selected is $\frac{3}{15}$

$\left(\text{this fraction could be simplified to } \frac{1}{5} \text{ but does not need to be}\right)$.

(b) There are 4 milk and 3 white chocolates. So the probability of
selecting a chocolate which is either milk or white is
$\frac{4+3}{15} = \frac{7}{15}$.

(c) The probability of selecting a milk chocolate is $\frac{4}{15}$ so the
probability of selecting a chocolate which is not milk will be
$1 - \frac{4}{15} = \frac{11}{15}$.

(d) It is impossible to select a chocolate which is a sugared
almond. So the probability of selecting a sugared almond is 0.

Example 2

The probability of a newly laid egg being cracked is 0.03.
Work out the probability of a newly laid egg not being cracked.

For the event 'laying an egg' the two outcomes 'cracked' and 'not
cracked' are mutually exclusive and they are the only two possible
outcomes.

So probability(cracked) + probability(not cracked) = 1
i.e. probability(not cracked) = 1 − probability(cracked)
$$= 1 - 0.03$$
$$= 0.97$$

Example 3

The diagram represents a biased, five-sided spinner.
Each section of the spinner is labelled with one of the letters
A, B, C, D and E.

The spinner is to be spun once.
It is biased and the probabilities of it landing on each of four of its
sections are given in the table below:

Section	A	B	C	D	E
Probability	0.22	0.31	0.16	0.14	

(a) Work out the probability that it will, when spun once, land on
section E.

(b) Work out the probability that it will, when spun once, land on a section labelled with a vowel.

(a) The sum of all the probabilities must be 1. So

$$0.22 + 0.31 + 0.16 + 0.14 + \text{Prob(E)} = 1$$
so $\quad 0.83 + \text{Prob(E)} = 1$
i.e. $\qquad \text{Prob(E)} = 1 - 0.83$
$\qquad \text{Prob(E)} = 0.17$

(b) To stop on a vowel, the spinner must stop on either A or E. These outcomes are mutually exclusive, so

$$\text{Prob(A or E)} = \text{Prob(A)} + \text{Prob(E)}$$
$$= 0.22 + 0.17$$
$$= 0.39$$

Exercise 11A   Links (*3C, 3D*) **3A, 3B, 3C, 3D**

1   A bag contains 12 equal-sized coloured balls. Five of the balls are red, 4 are blue and 3 are white.
A ball is to be selected at random.
Work out the probability of the selected ball being
   (a) blue   **(b)** either red or blue
   (c) green   **(d)** not red.

2   The probability of Jenny winning the raffle is $\dfrac{3}{1000}$.
Work out the probability of Jenny not winning the raffle.

3   The probability of a new DVD being faulty is 0.002.
Work out the probability of a new DVD not being faulty.

4   The probability of Lola getting an A* in Mathematics is 96%.
Work out the probability of Lola not getting an A* in Mathematics.

5   The diagram represents a six-sided dice.
Each face of the dice is labelled with one of the numbers 1, 2, 3, 4, 5 and 6.
The dice is biased.
When it is rolled once, the probabilities of the dice stopping with a certain number on its top face are partially given in the incomplete table below:

Face	1	2	3	4	5	6
Probability	0.13	0.17	0.18	0.12		0.20

The dice is rolled once.
   (a) Work out the probability of its top face showing 5.
   (b) Work out the probability of its top face showing a number less than 4.
   (c) Work out the probability of its top face showing a prime number.

6 An event has five mutually exclusive outcomes which are labelled A, B, C, D and E.
The incomplete table below provides information about the probabilities of some of these outcomes:

Outcome	A	B	C	D	E
Probability		0.33	0.17	0.21	0.08

Work out the probability for outcome A.

7 Patrick is an athlete.
On the school sports day he is entered for the 100 metres and the long jump.
It is estimated that

The probability of Patrick winning the 100 metres = 0.7
The probability of Patrick winning the long jump = 0.5

Explain fully what is wrong with the following statement:

'Using the OR rule the probability of Patrick winning the 100 metres or the long jump = 0.7 + 0.5 = 1.2.'

11.2 Listing outcomes

Teaching reference:
(*pp 257–259, section 19.1*)
pp 298–300, section 19.1

■ **Outcomes of a single or two successive events can be listed in a systematic way.**

Example 4

The diagram represents a fair spinner and a fair coin.
The five faces of the spinner are each labelled with one of the letters A, B, C, D and E.

The coin can land either Heads or Tails.

In a game, the spinner is to be spun once and the coin tossed once.

One possible outcome of these joint events is

(A, Heads)

(a) List all of the possible joint outcomes of these two events.

Lauren will win if the joint outcome is (A, Heads).

(b) Explain why the probability of Lauren winning is $\frac{1}{10}$.

(a) The joint outcomes are

(A, Heads) (B, Heads) (C, Heads) (D, Heads) (E, Heads)
(A, Tails)   (B, Tails)   (C, Tails)   (D, Tails)   (E, Tails)
There are 10 joint outcomes.

(b) Lauren has one chance of winning out of the 10 different outcomes. Each outcome is equally likely because the spinner and coin are fair.

So the probability of Lauren winning is $\frac{1}{10}$.

Exercise 11B   Links *(19A)* 19A

1 A football team can win, lose or draw a match.
The team plays two matches.
Write out the list of joint outcomes of the two matches.

2 A game is played with two spinners.
The spinners are shown in the diagram.
   (a) List all the possible joint outcomes when
      the spinners are each spun once.
   (b) Use your list to work out the probability
      of getting the joint outcome

        (Red, 3)

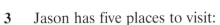

3 Jason has five places to visit:

    Leeds, York, Hull, Sheffield, Bolton

In each case he has three methods of travelling:

    Car, Train, Bus

One possible journey is

    Leeds by Bus

List all the possible journeys Jason could make.

4 The diagram represents a fair spinner and an ordinary fair
dice.

The spinner is to be spun once and the dice rolled once.
   (a) Make a list of all the joint outcomes.
   (b) Use your list to work out the probability of getting the
      joint outcome (A, 2).

5 Jim spins the spinner shown in the diagram twice.
He records the sum of the two numbers upon which the
spinner lands.
Show the results in the table below:

2nd spin

		1	2	3
1st spin	1			
	2			5
	3			

Summary of key points

■ Probability is measured on a scale from 0 to 1. You must write a probability as a fraction, a decimal or a percentage.

■ The estimated probability of an event or experiment

$$= \frac{\text{number of successful trials}}{\text{total number of trials}}$$

This is also called the *relative frequency*.

■ The calculated probability of an event happening

$$= \frac{\text{number of successful outcomes}}{\text{total number of possible outcomes}}$$

■ When one outcome prevents another outcome from happening the outcomes are mutually exclusive. The probabilities of all the possible mutually exclusive outcomes add up to 1.

When you toss a coin the outcomes Heads and Tails are mutually exclusive.

■ For two events A and B which are mutually exclusive
P(A or B) = P(A) + P(B)
This is called the OR rule.

■ If the probability of an event happening is p then the probability of the event not happening is $1 - p$.

■ If there are n mutually exclusive outcomes, all equally likely, the probability of one outcome happening is $\frac{1}{n}$.

■ If there are n mutually exclusive outcomes and a of these are deemed successful then the probability of a successful outcome is $\frac{a}{n}$.

■ When the outcome of one event does not affect the outcome of another event, they are called *independent* events.

When you toss a coin and roll a dice together the events are independent; one does not affect the other.

■ Outcomes of a single or two successive events can be listed in a systematic way.

Examination style practice paper

Section 1   You must not use a calculator.

1   **(a)** Write down all the prime numbers between 25
        and 35.   (2)
    (b) Find the lowest common multiple of 9 and 12.   (1)

2   In the Football League, a team gets 3 points for winning a
    match, 1 point for drawing a match and 0 points for losing a
    match.
    A team which wins (W) its first match and draws (D) its
    second match gets a total of 4 points.
    (a) Complete the table to show the numbers of points a team
        can get from two matches.

		Second match		
		W	**D**	**L**
	W		4	
First match	**D**			
	L			

                                                                   (2)

    Last season, Mathsville Rovers won x matches, drew y matches
    and lost l matches.
    (b) Write down an expression for the number of points
        Mathsville Rovers got last season.   (2)

3   **(a)** Work out $\frac{3}{4} + \frac{2}{3}$.   (2)
    (b) Work out $5\frac{2}{3} - 3\frac{4}{5}$.   (3)

4

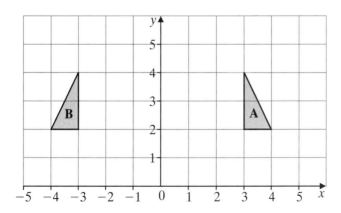

    (a) Describe fully the single transformation which maps
        triangle **A** onto triangle **B**.   (2)

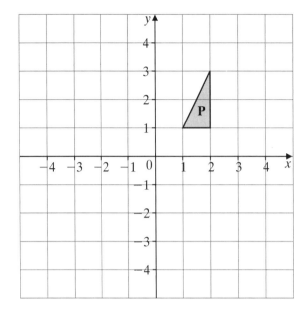

(b) Rotate triangle **P** through 180° about the point with
coordinates $(-1, 1)$. Label the image **Q**.   (2)

5   Here are four patterns of dots.

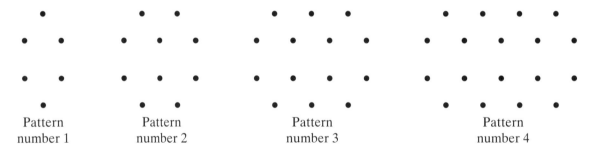

| Pattern | Pattern | Pattern | Pattern |
| number 1 | number 2 | number 3 | number 4 |

(a) Find an expression for the number of dots in pattern
number n.   (2)
(b) Find the pattern number of the pattern with 50 dots.   (1)

Section 2   You may use a calculator.

1   **(a)** Simplify $6p - 2q - 4p - 3q$.   (2)
    (b) Multiply $7c \times 3d$. Give your answer as simply as possible.
                                                                 (1)
    (c) Factorize $y^2 + 5y$.   (2)

2   Denise is going to carry out a survey into the favourite
television channels of the students in the secondary school she
attends. She wants to analyse her results according to the ages
of the students.
Design a suitable data collection table she could use to collect
the information.   (3)

3

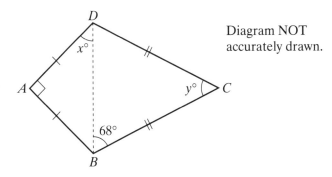

Diagram NOT accurately drawn.

The diagram shows a kite *ABCD*.
(a) Work out the size of the angle marked $x°$. (1)
(b) Work out the size of the angle marked $y°$. (2)

4 Chris scored 51 out of 75 in a test.
Express 51 out of 75 as a percentage. (2)

5

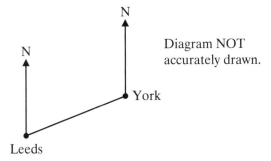

Diagram NOT accurately drawn.

The bearing of Leeds from York is 238°.
Work out the bearing of York from Leeds. (3)

6 Solve the equation $\dfrac{1 - 5x}{2} = 5 - x$. (3)

Answers

Exercise 1A

1. (a) 63, −63, 0
   (b) 562, −5620
   (c) 1 million, −2, 30 000
2. (a) Four hundred and thirty two
   (b) Eight thousand, two hundred
   (c) Six thousand, three hundred and seventy
   (d) Sixteen thousand, eight hundred and ninety two
   (e) Three hundred and seventy two thousand, eight hundred and fifty nine
   (f) Four hundred and eighty three thousand and two
   (g) Three million, two hundred and fifteen thousand, four hundred and sixty eight
   (h) Three million, six hundred and eighty two
3. (a) 463   (b) 15 027
   (c) 116 225   (d) 305 101
   (e) 2 327 035   (f) 500 000

Exercise 1B

1. (a) 7566   (b) 29 283
   (c) 15 164   (d) 45 648
   (e) 7675   (f) 16 180
2. (a) 24 remainder 2   (b) 56
   (c) 43   (d) 35 remainder 12
   (e) 69 remainder 2   (f) 46 remainder 2

Exercise 1C

1. (a) −7   (b) 4   (c) 10   (d) 9
   (e) −1   (f) 2   (g) −2   (h) −10
2. (a) 24   (b) −15   (c) −8   (d) 3
   (e) −40   (f) −6   (g) −30   (h) 10
3. 11 metres
4. −12°C
5. (a)

		1st number		
	×	−2	6	−7
	5	−10	30	−35
2nd number	−3	6	−18	21
	8	−16	48	−56

   (b)

		1st number		
	−	2	−3	8
	−4	6	1	12
2nd number	5	−3	−8	3
	−1	3	−2	9

   (c)

		1st number		
	+	−3	−4	2
	5	2	1	7
2nd number	1	−2	−3	3
	−6	−9	−10	−4

   (d)

		1st number		
	÷	16	−24	−36
	−2	−8	12	18
2nd number	4	4	−6	−9
	−8	−2	3	4.5

Exercise 1D

1. (a) 40   (b) 200   (c) 6000   (d) 3
   (e) 20   (f) 9000   (g) 2000   (h) 4000
2. (a) (i) 40 × 40   (ii) 1600
   (b) (i) 80 ÷ 20   (ii) 4
   (c) (i) 200 ÷ 40   (ii) 5
   (d) (i) 500 × 30   (ii) 15 000
   (e) (i) $\frac{900 \times 20}{10} = 90 \times 20$ (ii) 1800
   (f) (i) $\frac{30 \times 20}{10 \times 30}$ (ii) 2
3. 800 000
4. 2 × 20 = 40 pints

Exercise 1E

1. 1, 4, 9, 16, 25
2. 1, 8, 27, 64, 125
3. (a) 4.41   (b) 35.937
   (c) 2.4   (d) 3.5
   (e) 196   (f) 1000
   (g) 31   (h) 4913
   (i) 4   (j) 23 104
   (k) 25   (l) −6
   (m) 225   (n) 453.69
   (o) 0.6   (p) −0.9
   (q) 1   (r) 1
   (s) −1   (t) −1

Exercise 1F

1. (a) 33   (b) 4
   (c) 24   (d) 16
   (e) 2.7   (f) 81
   (g) 3   (h) 16
   (i) 1   (j) 6
   (k) 77   (l) 11
2. (a) 3 × (4 + 5) = 27
   (b) (2 + 3) × (2 + 3) = 25
   (c) (6 − 7) ÷ (8 − 9) = 1
   (d) 10 + 9 + 8 + 7 = 34
   (e) (3 − 3) × 3 = 0
   (f) (3 + 3) ÷ 3 = 2

Exercise 1G

1. (a) 1, 2, 3, 4, 6, 8, 12, 16, 24, 48
   (b) 1, 2, 3, 4, 5, 6, 8, 9, 10, 12, 15, 18, 20, 24, 30, 36, 40, 45, 60, 72, 90, 120, 180, 360
   (c) 1, 29
   (d) 1, 2, 4, 5, 10, 20, 25, 50, 100
   (e) 1, 71
   (f) 1, 3, 5, 15, 43, 129, 215, 645
2. 29, 71
3. (a) 4, 8, 12, 16, 20
   (b) 7, 14, 21, 28, 35
   (c) 11, 22, 33, 44, 55
   (d) 20, 40, 60, 80, 100
4. (a) 2×5^2 (b) $2^3 \times 3^2$
   (c) $2 \times 3^2 \times 5^2$ (d) $2^3 \times 3 \times 5 \times 7$
5. (a) 3   (b) 2   (c) 4
   (d) 3   (e) 4
6. (a) 24   (b) 35   (c) 12
   (d) 12   (e) 30

Exercise 1H

1. (a) 256 214; 0; three hundred and two thousand four hundred and twelve; −73 864
   (b) Two hundred and fifty six thousand two hundred and fourteen
   (c) 302 412
2. (a) 10 591   (b) 23 646
   (c) 31   (d) 53
3. (a) −9   (b) 10
   (c) 4   (d) 2
4. (a) −16   (b) 2
   (c) −2   (d) 35
5. (a) (i) $\frac{300 \times 20}{500}$ (ii) 12
   (b) (i) $\frac{2 \times 8}{2^2}$ (ii) 4
   (c) (i) $\frac{8000 \div 400}{\sqrt[3]{8}}$ (ii) 10
6. £600
7. (a) 1, 9, 81
   (b) 1, 27
   (c) 13, 17, 23, 31
   (d) 1, 9, 27
   (e) 9, 27, 81
8. (a) 25   (b) 100
   (c) 64   (d) 4
   (e) 6   (f) 8
   (g) 39.69   (h) 13.824
   (i) 2.4   (j) −2
9. (a) 32   (b) 5   (c) 7   (d) 2
10. (a) $2^2 \times 3^2 \times 5$ (b) $2^2 \times 7^2$
    (c) $2^3 \times 3 \times 5^2$
11. (a) 6   (b) 6   (c) 3
12. (a) 20   (b) 24   (c) 24

Exercise 2A

1. (a) $\frac{1}{3} = \frac{2}{6} = \frac{4}{12} = \frac{6}{18}$
   (b) $\frac{2}{5} = \frac{4}{10} = \frac{20}{50} = \frac{40}{100}$
   (c) $\frac{3}{8} = \frac{6}{16} = \frac{12}{32} = \frac{24}{64}$
   (d) $\frac{3}{10} = \frac{15}{50} = \frac{30}{100} = \frac{300}{1000}$
2. (a) $\frac{1}{2}$ (b) $\frac{3}{5}$ (c) $\frac{2}{3}$ (d) $\frac{3}{5}$ (e) $\frac{5}{6}$
   (f) $\frac{4}{5}$ (g) $\frac{3}{5}$ (h) $\frac{4}{5}$ (i) $\frac{2}{3}$ (j) $\frac{5}{6}$

Exercise 2B

1. (a) $\frac{3}{2}$ (b) $\frac{5}{4}$ (c) $\frac{7}{5}$ (d) $\frac{7}{3}$ (e) $\frac{15}{4}$
   (f) $\frac{23}{5}$ (g) $\frac{59}{10}$ (h) $\frac{83}{10}$ (i) $\frac{87}{8}$ (j) $\frac{285}{28}$
2. (a) $3\frac{1}{2}$ (b) $2\frac{1}{4}$ (c) $2\frac{1}{8}$ (d) $3\frac{1}{5}$ (e) $6\frac{1}{2}$
   (f) $2\frac{3}{10}$ (g) $4\frac{3}{5}$ (h) $5\frac{1}{3}$ (i) $2\frac{1}{10}$ (j) $7\frac{1}{2}$

Exercise 2C

1. (a) $1\frac{1}{4}$ (b) $\frac{11}{15}$ (c) $\frac{7}{36}$ (d) $\frac{9}{14}$
   (e) $1\frac{3}{10}$ (f) $\frac{13}{28}$ (g) $\frac{19}{28}$ (h) $\frac{1}{8}$
2. (a) $1\frac{3}{4}$ (b) $3\frac{1}{2}$ (c) $4\frac{1}{12}$ (d) $3\frac{1}{2}$
   (e) $5\frac{13}{15}$ (f) $6\frac{7}{12}$ (g) $4\frac{11}{12}$ (h) $5\frac{13}{21}$
3. (a) $1\frac{5}{8}$ (b) $2\frac{1}{12}$ (c) $1\frac{7}{24}$ (d) $3\frac{7}{10}$
   (e) $2\frac{3}{4}$ (f) $4\frac{7}{10}$ (g) $1\frac{11}{14}$ (h) $3\frac{11}{24}$
4. $10\frac{1}{4}$ lb
5. $3\frac{7}{8}$ kg   6. $1\frac{1}{8}$ metres   7. $2\frac{5}{12}$ kg

Exercise 2D

1 (a) $\frac{2}{15}$ (b) $\frac{1}{2}$ (c) $\frac{3}{10}$ (d) $\frac{1}{2}$ (e) $\frac{5}{6}$
(f) $1\frac{5}{6}$ (g) $\frac{4}{11}$ (h) $\frac{1}{9}$ (i) $1\frac{1}{5}$ (j) $1\frac{1}{4}$

2 (a) $1\frac{1}{8}$ (b) $2\frac{3}{4}$ (c) $5\frac{5}{18}$ (d) $16\frac{1}{5}$
(e) $3\frac{1}{4}$ (f) $10\frac{4}{5}$ (g) $3\frac{3}{4}$ (h) $\frac{3}{4}$

3 (a) $1\frac{1}{11}$ (b) $1\frac{11}{13}$ (c) $1\frac{9}{11}$ (d) $1\frac{13}{17}$
(e) $3\frac{1}{7}$ (f) $8\frac{1}{6}$ (g) 12 (h) $13\frac{1}{3}$

4 8

5 $7\frac{1}{8}$ kg

6 $1\frac{1}{2}$ hours

7 $3\frac{1}{14}$

Exercise 2E

1 (a) 53.1 (b) 0.216
(c) 0.5358 (d) 267.1
(e) 3.6 (f) 0.0053
(g) 638 (h) 280
(i) 0.003 (j) 0.00786

2 (a) 3.6 kg
(b) 0.0036 kg or 3.6 g

3 11.3 g

4 3568 g

Exercise 2F

1 (a) 6.2, 0.62, 0.6, 0.59
(b) 7.9, 0.79, 0.76, 0.079
(c) 3.27, 3.21, 3.12, 0.37
(d) 1.01, 0.99, 0.91, 0.09
(e) 0.024, 0.021, 0.02, 0.002

2 Keith 1.52
Julie 1.60
Karen 1.67
Graham 1.68

3 3.6 s, 3.62 s, 3.902 s, 3.96 s

Exercise 2G

1 (a) 1.5 (b) 0.42
(c) 0.468 (d) 0.3303
(e) 7.62 (f) 4.716
(g) 59.94 (h) 0.22784

2 (a) 2.6 (b) 52.3
(c) 7.125 (d) 17.6
(e) 2.95 (f) 23.44
(g) 7.3125 (h) 20.375

3 4.68 m

4 3 kg

5 5 glasses

6 146.2 km

7 18 stamps

Exercise 2H

1 (a) 0.6 (b) $0.1\dot{6}$
(c) 0.625 (d) 0.45
(e) 0.75 (f) $0.\dot{3}$
(g) 0.4 (h) $0.58\dot{3}$
(i) $0.31\dot{8}$ (j) $0.25\dot{9}$

2 (a) $\frac{7}{10}$ (b) $\frac{1}{2}$
(c) $\frac{3}{25}$ (d) $\frac{13}{20}$
(e) $\frac{5}{6}$ (f) $\frac{181}{500}$
(g) $\frac{137}{1000}$ (h) $\frac{137}{200}$

3 (a) exact
(b) recurring
(c) exact
(d) recurring
(e) recurring

Exercise 2I

1 (a) $\frac{13}{25}$, 0.7, $\frac{8}{10}$, 0.81, 0.84
(b) $\frac{1}{2}$, 0.7, 0.73, $\frac{3}{4} = 0.75$
(c) 2, 2.3, $2\frac{4}{10}$, 2.42, $2\frac{43}{100}$
(d) 0.3, 0.33, $\frac{1}{3}$, 0.34, $\frac{7}{20}$
(e) 4, 4.04, $4\frac{4}{10}$, 4.44, $4\frac{4}{9}$

2 (a) 1.3 kg, 1.32 kg, 1.39 kg, 1.41 kg
(b) 9.9 s, 9.92 s, 10.01 s, 10.1 s, 10.11 s
(c) $\frac{1}{4}$ kg, 0.3 kg, 0.35 kg, $\frac{1}{2}$ kg
(d) $\frac{1}{6}$ inch, $\frac{1}{4}$ inch, $\frac{3}{8}$ inch, $\frac{2}{5}$ inch

Exercise 2J

1 (a) 17.5 pints (b) 17.14 l
2 (a) 11 lb (b) 20 kg
3 42.5 cm **4** 48 km **5** 56.3 l

Exercise 2K

1 (a) $\frac{1}{2} = \frac{4}{8}$ (b) $\frac{3}{4} = \frac{12}{16}$ (c) $\frac{5}{8} = \frac{15}{24}$

2 (a) $\frac{2}{3}$ (b) $\frac{9}{11}$ (c) $\frac{3}{4}$ (d) $\frac{3}{4}$

3 (a) $\frac{7}{4}$ (b) $\frac{16}{7}$ (c) $\frac{29}{8}$

4 (a) $1\frac{3}{5}$ (b) $2\frac{1}{6}$ (c) $3\frac{4}{7}$

5 (a) $1\frac{7}{24}$ (b) $\frac{7}{20}$ (c) $5\frac{13}{20}$
(d) $1\frac{1}{12}$ (e) $4\frac{11}{42}$ (f) $1\frac{3}{8}$

6 $2\frac{1}{2}$ kg

7 $\frac{3}{4}$ hours

8 (a) $\frac{1}{2}$ (b) $\frac{4}{5}$ (c) $3\frac{3}{4}$
(d) $\frac{2}{7}$ (e) $2\frac{10}{27}$ (f) $4\frac{2}{5}$

9 6 lessons
10 2 pints
11 (a) 3.13 (b) 43.8 (c) 0.0256
(d) 20 (e) 0.0056 (f) 2130
12 37.5 kg
13 0.0068 kg
14 (a) 4.264 (b) 4.4
(c) 83.46 (d) 3.6
15 15 servings
16 £7.62
17 (a) 0.8 (b) 0.875 (c) $0.\dot{5}$
18 (a) $\frac{4}{25}$ (b) $\frac{3}{5}$ (c) $\frac{97}{200}$
19 (a) 3.3, 3, $\frac{3}{4}$, $\frac{3}{8}$, 0.3
(b) $0.\dot{7}$, 0.77, $\frac{3}{4}$, $\frac{37}{50}$, $\frac{7}{10}$
20 (a) 25 miles (b) 192 km
21 67.5 litres

Exercise 3A

1 (a) (i) 0.65 (ii) $\frac{13}{20}$
(b) (i) 0.2 (ii) $\frac{1}{5}$
(c) (i) 0.25 (ii) $\frac{1}{4}$
(d) (i) 0.32 (ii) $\frac{8}{25}$
(e) (i) 0.74 (ii) $\frac{37}{50}$
(f) (i) 0.225 (ii) $\frac{9}{40}$
(g) (i) 0.675 (ii) $\frac{27}{40}$
(h) (i) $0.\dot{3}$ (ii) $\frac{1}{3}$
(i) (i) $0.\dot{6}$ (ii) $\frac{2}{3}$
(j) (i) 0.0525 (ii) $\frac{21}{400}$

2 (a) 50% (b) 60%
(c) 23% (d) 35%
(e) 85% (f) 30%
(g) 57.5% (h) 22.5%
(i) 2.25% (j) 83.3%

3

Fraction	Decimal	Percentage
$\frac{3}{20}$	**0.15**	15%
$\frac{7}{10}$	**0.7**	**70%**
$\frac{8}{25}$	0.32	**32%**
$\frac{7}{8}$	**0.875**	87.5%
$\frac{1}{6}$	$0.1\dot{6}$	$16\frac{2}{3}\%$

Exercise 3B

1 (a) 27 (b) 42
(c) 11 (d) 9
(e) £1.80 (f) £9
(g) £8.75 (h) 262.5 kg
(i) 10 g (j) £17.91
2 (a) 78 girls (b) 72 boys
3 10.5 g **4** £2310 **5** 156
6 £4.50 **7** £1.50

Exercise 3C

1 (a) £31.50 (b) £51
2 £470 **3** £44 800 **4** £297
5 £254.40 **6** £11 480 **7** £18 962.50
8 £270.25

Exercise 3D

1 90% **2** 80%
3 (a) 26% (b) 38.4% (c) 35.6%
4 (a) $66\frac{2}{3}\%$ (b) $33\frac{1}{3}\%$
5 20% **6** 17.5% **7** 25%
8 20% **9** 37.5% **10** 22%

Exercise 3E

1

Fraction	Decimal	Percentage
$\frac{3}{5}$	**0.6**	**60%**
$\frac{6}{25}$	**0.24**	24%
$\frac{13}{40}$	0.325	**32.5%**
$\frac{5}{6}$	**$0.8\dot{3}$**	$83.\dot{3}\%$

2 (a) 24 (b) £2.40 (c) £6 (d) 60 g
3 (a) 68 (b) 12
4 £423 **5** £37.40
6 80% **7** 65%
8 Increase of 10 g is a 12.5% increase on the 80 g cereal bar.

Exercise 4A

1

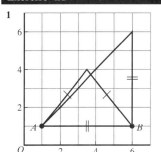

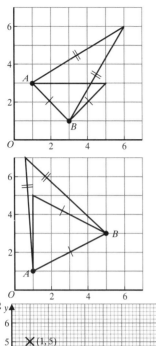

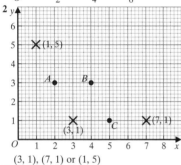

2

(3, 1), (7, 1) or (1, 5)

3

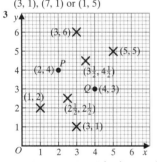

(3, 6) and (5, 5) or $(3\frac{1}{2}, 4\frac{1}{2})$ and $(2\frac{1}{2}, 2\frac{1}{2})$ or (1, 2) and (3, 1)

4

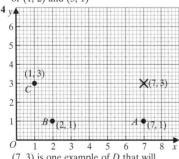

(7, 3) is one example of D that will make a trapezium

5

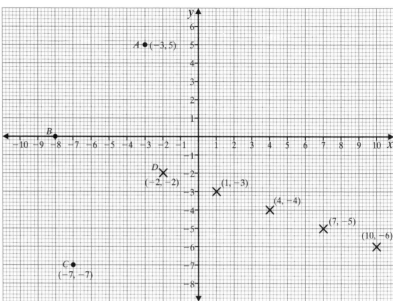

$D\ (-2, -2)$
For a kite the points could be:
(1, −3) (4, −4) (7, −5) (10, −6)

Exercise 4B

1. $5x - 4y$
2. $-2a + 3b$
3. $8p - 5q$
4. $10s + 2t$
5. $-c - 7d$
6. $6c + d$
7. $5ab$
8. $3cd$
9. $5pq$
10. $a^2 + 4a$
11. $5b^2 + b$
12. $2c^2 + 3c$
13. $a^3 + 2a^2 + 3a$
14. $5a + 3ab + 4b$
15. $-x + 5xy$

Exercise 4C

1. $5x + 14$
2. $20x + 17$
3. $23x + 14$
4. $-8x + 12$ or $12 - 8x$
5. $9 - 21x$
6. $15 - 23x$
7. $12x - 22y$
8. $22y - 2x$
9. $-4x - 21y$
10. $x + 4y$
11. $7y + 2$
12. 27
13. $x - 3$
14. $7y - 16x + 6$
15. $21x - 19y$
16. $21y - 27x$
17. $10x - 7y$
18. $20x - 32y$
19. $8xy + 3x$
20. $8xy + 2x + y$
21. $6x - 4y - 3xy$
22. $10xy - 20x^2 - 6y^2$
23. $9ab - 6a^2 - 4b^2$
24. $11pq + 18p^2$
25. $13c^2 + 12cd$
26. $21cd - 15c^2$
27. $a^2 + 2ab + b^2$
28. $5ab + ac - 2bc$
29. $5ab + 5ac + 5bc$
30. $-4ab - 4ac - 9bc$

Exercise 4D

1. $3(x + 4)$
2. $7(x - 3)$
3. $5(3x + 4)$
4. $3(3x - 4)$
5. $2(2x + 3)$
6. $3(3x - 5)$
7. $6(2x + 3)$
8. $7(3 + 4x)$
9. $7(2 + 3y)$
10. $5(7x - 3)$
11. $3(2x - y)$
12. $7(2x + y)$
13. $5(2x - y)$
14. $5(5a + 3b)$
15. $3(a - 3b)$
16. $17(p + 3q)$
17. $9(4c - d)$
18. $8(3s + 2t)$
19. $x(x + 6y)$
20. $x(2x - 3y)$
21. $y(4x + y)$
22. $a(5b - a)$
23. $b(6c + b)$
24. $b(4b + 5c)$
25. $b(3a - 5c)$
26. $x(x + 3y)$
27. $3x(x - 3y)$
28. $4p(2p + q)$
29. $7x(2x + 3y)$
30. $5b(2a - 3c)$
31. $2a(2a - 3bc)$
32. $2x^2(x + 2y)$

Exercise 4E

(a) Equation
(b) Equation
(c) Expression
(d) Formula
(e) Formula
(f) Expression
(g) Identity
(h) Identity

Exercise 4F

1 (a) (i) 68°F   (ii) 113°F   (iii) 158°F
   (b) (i) 100°C   (ii) 50°C   (iii) 25°C
2 9 trees
3 (a) 300 cm^2
   (b) 195 cm^2
   (c) 10.585 cm^2
   (d) 14.95 cm^2
4 (a) 261.8 cm^3
   (b) 769.7 cm^3
   (c) 203.9 cm^3
5 (a) 56 m/s
   (b) −52 m/s
   (c) −124 m/s

Exercise 4G

1 (a) $4a$
   (b) $4b$
   (c) $3c - 4d$
   (d) $p - 5q$
   (e) $-x - y$
2 (a) $6a - 15x$
   (b) $a^3 + 2a^2b$
   (c) $2bc - 10bd$
   (d) $6b^2 + 6ab$
   (e) $6x^2 - 3x^2y$
3 (a) $4(x - 3)$ (b) $4(2a^2 + 3b)$
   (c) $3x(2x + 3y)$ (d) $ab(a - b)$
   (e) $3pq(p + 5)$
4 (a) 57 m
   (b) −100 m
   (c) −594 m
5 (a) Formula   (b) Identity
   (c) Expression   (d) Equation
   (e) Formula   (f) Expression

Exercise 5A

1 $a = 9$ 2 $b = 4$
3 $c = 15$ 4 $d = 3$
5 $e = 3$ 6 $f = 16$
7 $g = 6$ 8 $h = 20$
9 $m = 11$ 10 $n = 6$
11 $p = 3\frac{1}{2}$ 12 $q = -1$
13 $t = 0$ 14 $v = \frac{1}{3}$
15 $x = -3$ 16 $y = 2\frac{3}{4}$
17 $a = -12$ 18 $b = 0$
19 $c = 4$ 20 $d = -1$

Exercise 5B

1 $a = 12$ 2 $b = 5$
3 $c = 24$ 4 $d = 7$
5 $e = 6$ 6 $f = 16$
7 $g = 6$ 8 $h = 21$
9 $m = 7$ 10 $n = 15$
11 $p = \frac{1}{3}$ 12 $q = 0$
13 $t = -4$ 14 $v = \frac{4}{5}$
15 $x = -6$ 16 $y = 1\frac{2}{3}$
17 $a = -1$ 18 $b = 4\frac{1}{2}$
19 $c = \frac{2}{3}$ 20 $d = -2$

Exercise 5C

1 $a = 4$ 2 $b = 3$
3 $c = 6$ 4 $d = 7$
5 $d = 2$ 6 $e = \frac{1}{2}$
7 $f = -4$ 8 $n = \frac{11}{3}$
9 $p = 0$ 10 $q = \frac{-9}{5}$

Exercise 5D

1 $x = 2$ 2 $x = 4$
3 $x = 3$ 4 $x = 2$
5 $x = 1$ 6 $x = 3$
7 $x = 1$ 8 $x = 4$
9 $x = 8$ 10 $x = 2$
11 $x = 1$ 12 $x = 4$
13 $x = -3$ 14 $x = 0$
15 $x = 2\frac{1}{2}$ 16 $x = \frac{3}{5}$
17 $x = -1$ 18 $x = 1\frac{2}{3}$
19 $x = -2$ 20 $x = -\frac{2}{3}$

Exercise 5E

1 8
2 $a = 40$, largest angle is 80°
3 12
4 130°, 80°, 150°
5 8 cm, 9 cm, 7 cm
6 11
7 $y = 7$
8 52
9 15 cm
10 $x = 6$ $y = 4$

Exercise 5F

1 $a = 40$ 2 $b = 24$
3 $c = 23$ 4 $d = 18$
5 $e = 11$ 6 $m = 18$
7 $n = 23$ 8 $p = 12$
9 $y = 6$ 10 $z = 8$
11 $q = -8$ 12 $t = 10\frac{1}{2}$
13 $v = -\frac{2}{3}$ 14 $w = 1$
15 $x = -1$ 16 $y = \frac{1}{2}$
17 $z = -\frac{1}{2}$ 18 $x = \frac{3}{4}$
19 $y = 1\frac{3}{4}$ 20 $x = 14\frac{1}{2}$

Exercise 5G

1 $x = \pm 7$ 2 $x = \pm 8$
3 $x = \pm 5$ 4 $x = \pm 3$
5 $x = \pm 6$ 6 $x = \pm 3$
7 $x = \pm 2$ 8 $x = \pm\frac{3}{8}$
9 $x = \pm\frac{5}{2}$ 10 $x = \pm\frac{1}{2}$
11 $x = \pm\frac{3}{7}$ 12 $x = \pm\frac{6}{5}$
13 $x = \pm\frac{1}{4}$ 14 $x = \pm\frac{9}{2}$
15 $x = \pm 2$

Exercise 5H

1 $a = 4$ 2 $b = 8$
3 $c = \frac{1}{4}$ 4 $d = \frac{1}{8}$
5 $e = \frac{5}{2} = 2\frac{1}{2}$ 6 $p = \frac{2}{5}$
7 $t = \frac{1}{5}$ 8 $t = \frac{3}{2}$
9 $x = \frac{3}{8}$ 10 $y = \frac{8}{3} = 2\frac{2}{3}$

Exercise 5I

1 $a = 3$ 2 $b = -1$
3 $c = \frac{2}{3}$ 4 $d = 3\frac{1}{2}$
5 $e = 2$ 6 $f = \frac{5}{2} = 2\frac{1}{2}$
7 $g = \frac{1}{4}$ 8 $h = -3$
9 $m = 0$ 10 $n = 2$
11 $p = 4$ 12 $x = 5$
13 $y = 54$ 14 $z = -7$
15 $q = -2$ 16 $t = \frac{1}{2}$

17 $u = -13$ 18 $v = 1$
19 $w = \frac{3}{4}$ 20 $a = \pm 2$
21 $b = \pm\frac{8}{3}$ 22 $c = 8$
23 $d = \frac{3}{8}$ 24 18
25 48 cm

Exercise 6A

1 (i) 4, 6, 8, ...   even numbers
   (ii) 10, 15, 20, ...   multiples of 5
   (iii) 4, 8, 16, ...   powers of 2
2 (a) 15, 11, 7, ...
   (b) 25, 5, 1, ...
   (c) 7, 31, 127, ...
   (d) 8, 12, 28, ...
   (e) 32, 20, 14
3 (i) add 6;   37, 43, ...
   (ii) subtract 7;   8, 1, ...
   (iii) multiply by 5;   1250, 6250, ...
   (iv) divide by 2;   4, 2, ...
4 (i) 54, 63, ...   multiples of 9
   (ii) 100 000, 1000 000 ...   powers of 10
5 (i) 5, −1, ...   subtract 6
   (ii) 1, $\frac{1}{10}$, ...   divide by 10
   (iii) −1, 2, ...   add 3
   (iv) $\frac{1}{4}$, $\frac{1}{16}$, ...   divide by 4
6 (a) 35
   (b) 67
   (c) 68
   (d) 72
7 (a) 3, 5, 7, 9, ...
   (b) Each difference is 2 more than the previous difference.
   (c) 36, 49, 64, 81, 100, ...
8 (a) 2, 3, 4, 5, ...
   (b) Each difference is 1 more than previous difference.
   (c) 21, 28, 36, 45, 55, ...

Exercise 6B

1 (i)   (a) 3, 8, 13, 18, 23, ...
       (b) 58
   (ii)   (a) 12, 18, 24, 30, 36, ...
       (b) 78
   (iii) (a) 11, 19, 27, 35, 43, ...
       (b) 99
   (iv) (a) 13, 10, 7, 4, 1, ...
       (b) −20
2 (i) $5n - 2$
   (ii) $6(n + 1)$
   (iii) $8n + 3$
   (iv) $16 - 3n$
3 (i)   (a) 8, 16, 24, 32, 40, ...
       (b) 96
   (ii)   (a) 3, 5, 7, 9, 11, ...
       (b) 25
   (iii) (a) 1, 6, 11, 16, 21, ...
       (b) 56
   (iv) (a) 37, 34, 31, 28, 25, ...
       (b) 4
   (v)   (a) 13, 7, 1, −5, −11
       (b) −53
4 (a) $9n$ (b) $5n + 4$
   (c) $n + 11$ (d) $25 - 4n$
   (e) $10n - 7$ (f) $9 - n$
   (g) $31 - 8n$ (h) $9n - 21$
5 (a) $2n$ (b) $2n - 1$
   (c) $8n$ (d) $2n + 4$
   (e) $2n + 7$ (f) $5n + 20$

Exercise 6C

1 (i) (a) 16, 19
  (b) $3n + 1$
  (c) 61
  (d) 35
 (ii) (a) 26, 31
  (b) $5n + 1$
  (c) 101
  (d) 21
 (iii) (a) 36, 43
  (b) $7n + 1$
  (c) 141
  (d) 15
2 (a) The coefficient n is 1 less than the number of matchsticks in shape 1, since each successive shape that is joined has as its number of matchsticks 1 less than the original shape's number of matchsticks.
  (b) $11n + 1$
3 (a) 20, 24   (b) $4n$
  (c) 124   (d) 23
4 (a) 16, 18
  (b) $2n + 6$
  (c) 44
  (d) 26
5 (a) 17, 20
  (b) $3n + 2$
  (c) 71
  (d) 26
6 (a) 17, 21
  (b) $4n - 3$
  (c) 97
  (d) 19
  (e) 13
7 (a) 22, 26
  (b) $4n + 2$
  (c) 150
  (d) 21
  (e) 24
8 (a) 16, 19
  (b) $3n + 1$
  (c) 79
  (d) 31
  (e) 19

Exercise 6D

1 (a) 20, 27, 34, ...
  (b) 12, 48, 192, ...
  (c) 29, 173, 1037, ...
  (d) 12, 14, 18, ...
2 (i) (a) Each term is 8 more than the previous term
  (b) 43, 51
 (ii) (a) Each term is $\frac{1}{2} \times$ the previous term
  (b) $\frac{1}{4}, \frac{1}{8}$
 (iii) (a) Each term is 4 less than the previous term
  (b) 0, −4
 (iv) (a) Each difference is 2 times the previous one
  (b) 127, 255
3 (i) (a) 12, 19, 26, 33, 40
  (b) 75
  (c) $7n + 5$
 (ii) (a) 1, 10, 19, 28, 37
  (b) 82
  (c) $9n - 8$
 (iii) (a) 15, 10, 5, 0, −5
  (b) −30
  (c) $20 - 5n$

4 (i) (a) 9, 18, 27, 36, 45 ...
  (b) 180
 (ii) (a) 10, 13, 16, 19, 22 ...
  (b) 67
 (iii) (a) −6, −1, 4, 9, 14 ...
  (b) 89
 (iv) (a) 21, 14, 7, 0, −7
  (b) −112
 (v) (a) −1, −10, −19, −28, −37
  (b) −172
5 (a) $6n + 1$
  (b) $26 - 3n$
  (c) $7n - 7$
  (d) $14 - 9n$
6 13
7 18
8 6
9 35
10 (a) 26, 31
  (b) $5n + 1$
  (c) 91
  (d) 13
  (e) 19
11 (a) 21, 25
  (b) $3n + 1$
  (c) $4n + 1$
  (d) 31
  (e) 69
  (f) 28
  (g) 73

Exercise 7A

1 pentagon
2 hexagon
3 quadrilateral
4 triangle
5 nonagon
6 heptagon

Exercise 7B

1 right-angled triangle
2 equilateral triangle
3 isosceles triangle
4 isosceles triangle
5 right-angled triangle
6 isosceles
7 equilateral triangle
8 obtuse scalene triangle

Exercise 7C

1 trapezium
2 square
3 rectangle
4 parallelogram
5 square
6 kite
7 trapezium
8 parallelogram
9 arrowhead
10 trapezium
11 (a) rectangle, square
  (b) parallelogram, rhombus, rectangle, square
  (c) arrowhead
  (d) parallelogram, rhombus, rectangle, square
  (e) kite, arrowhead

12 (a)
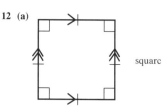
square

(b)
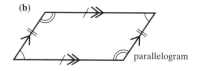
parallelogram

(c)
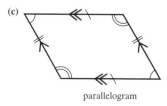
parallelogram

(d)
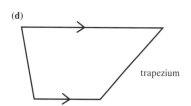
trapezium

Exercise 7D

1
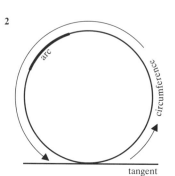

2

3

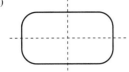

Exercise 8A

1 (a)

(b)

(c)

(d)

 no lines of symmetry

(e)

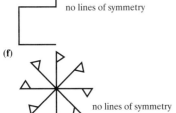 no lines of symmetry

(f)

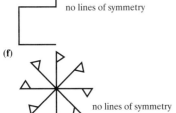 no lines of symmetry

2 (a) 2
   (b) 3
   (c) 2
   (d) no rotational symmetry
   (e) 2
   (f) 8

3 (a)

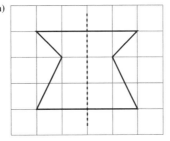

(b)

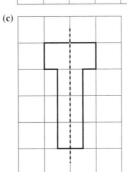

(c)

(d)

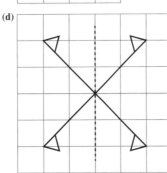

(e)

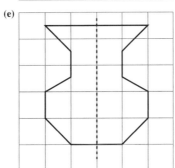

(f)

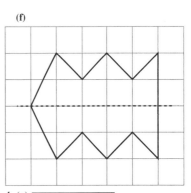

4 (a)

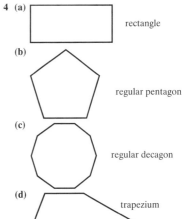 rectangle

(b)

regular pentagon

(c)

regular decagon

(d)

trapezium

Exercise 8B

1
   (a)

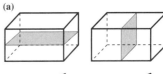

   (b)

   (c)

   (d)

 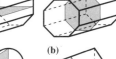

2 (a)   **(b)**

This shape actually
has an infinite
number of planes
of symmetry.

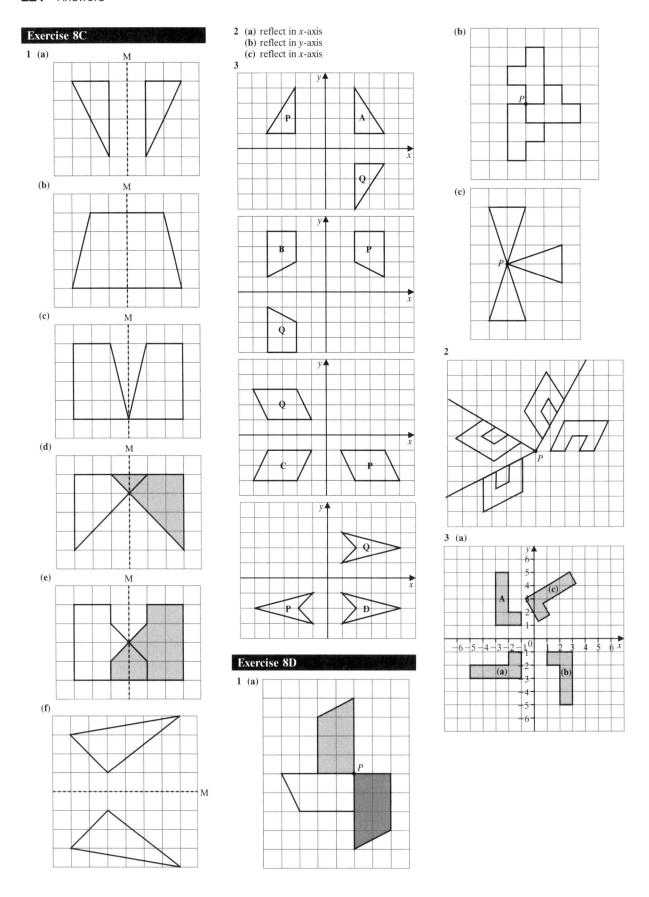

Exercise 8C

1 (a) M

(b) M

(c) M

(d) M

(e) M

(f) M

2 (a) reflect in x-axis
  (b) reflect in y-axis
  (c) reflect in x-axis

3

Exercise 8D

1 (a)

(b)

(c)

2

3 (a)

(b)

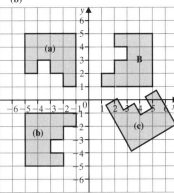

(c)

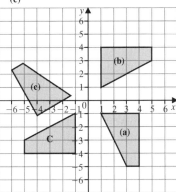

(d)

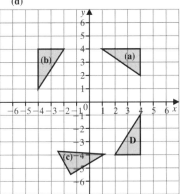

4 (a) Rotation of 90° anti-clockwise, around the origin.
(b) Rotation of 180°, around the origin.
(c) Rotation of 90° clockwise, around the origin.

Exercise 8E

1

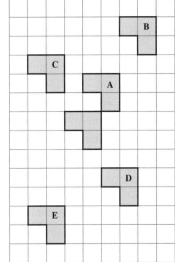

2 $\begin{pmatrix} 5 \\ -1 \end{pmatrix}$ translates **P** to **R**

$\begin{pmatrix} 9 \\ -3 \end{pmatrix}$ translates **P** to **S**

$\begin{pmatrix} 13 \\ 0 \end{pmatrix}$ translates **P** to **T**

$\begin{pmatrix} 5 \\ -5 \end{pmatrix}$ translates **P** to **V**

3 $\begin{pmatrix} 1 \\ -6 \end{pmatrix}$ translates **T** onto **A**

$\begin{pmatrix} 7 \\ -0 \end{pmatrix}$ translates **T** onto **B**

$\begin{pmatrix} 5 \\ -4 \end{pmatrix}$ translates **T** onto **C**

$\begin{pmatrix} -2 \\ -2 \end{pmatrix}$ translates **T** onto **D**

4

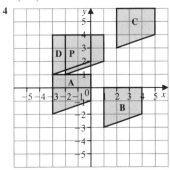

Exercise 9A

1 (a) 27 mm, 2.7 cm
(b) 39 mm, 3.9 cm
(c) 51 mm, 5.1 cm
(d) 42 mm, 4.2 cm
(e) 81 mm, 8.1 cm

2 (a) ————————————
  (b) ——————————————
  (c) ————————————
  (d) ——————————————————
  (e) ————————————————

3 (a)

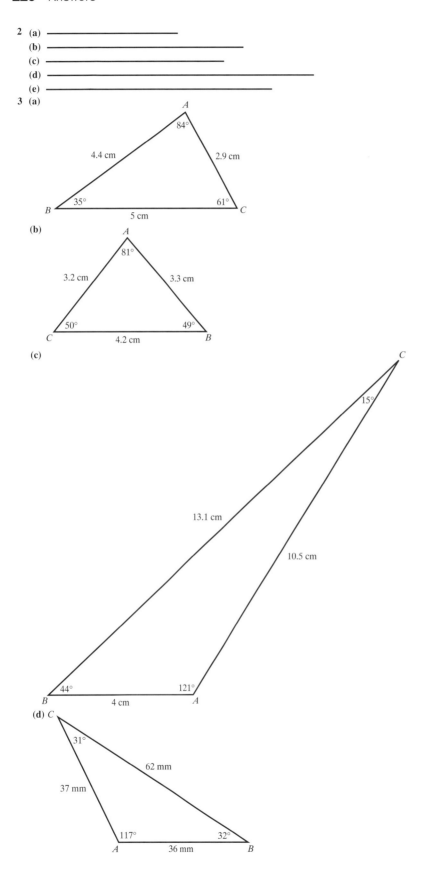

4 **(a)**

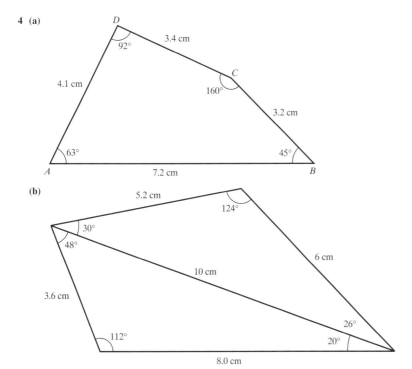

(b)

Exercise 9B

1

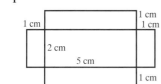

scale 1 cm : 2 cm

2

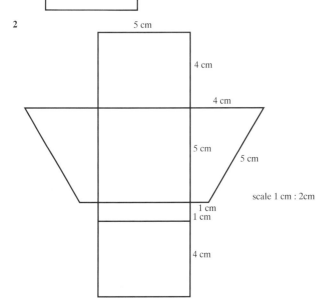

scale 1 cm : 2cm

3

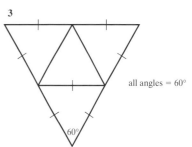

all angles = 60°

4

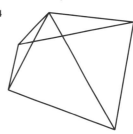

pyramid with trapezium as base
5 Yes, since the length of the rectangle is the same as the 'length' of the semi-circle.

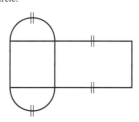

6 **(a)**, **(c)**, **(e)** and **(f)**

Exercise 9C

1 **(a)** $a = 64°$ **(b)** $b = 72°$
 (c) $c = 52°$ **(d)** $e = 68°$
 $d = 76°$
2 **(a)** $a = 48°$ **(b)** $x = 20°$
 (c) $b = 30°$ **(d)** $y = 25°$
 (e) $x = 18°$
3 $a = 46°$ (corresponding angles (parallel lines))
4 $b = 53°$ (alternate angles (parallel lines))
5 $c = 127°$ (corresponding angles (parallel lines), vertically opposite angles)
6 $d = 102°$ (vertically opposite angles, corresponding angles, base angles of an isosceles triangle, angles of a triangle add up to 180°)
7 $e = 20.5°$ (base angles of an isosceles triangle, vertically opposite angles.)
8 $f + 25° + 60° = 180°$
 $f = 95°$ (vertically opposite angles, angles of a triangle add up to 180°)
 $g = 120°$ (angles on a straight line, corresponding angles)
9 $h = 44°$ (corresponding angles, angles of a straight line)
 $i = 74°$ (angles of a triangle add up to 180°, corresponding angles)
10 $k = 47°$ (alternate angles)
 $m = 99°$ (angles of a triangle add up to 180°)
 $n = 81°$ (alternate angles, angles on a straight line)

Exercise 9D

1 (a) 40°   **(b)** 140°
Sum of interior angles = 1260°
2 24 sides
3 10
4 (a) $a = 91°$
(b) $b = 110°$
   $c = 110°$
   $e = 70°$
   $d = 70°$
(c) $f = 60°$
   $g = 120°$
5 angle $B = z$ (corresponding angles)
angle $A = y$ (alternate angles)
$x + y + z = 180°$ (angles on a straight line)
∴ angle A + angle B + angle $x = 180°$
6

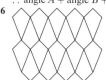

Exercise 9E

1 (a)

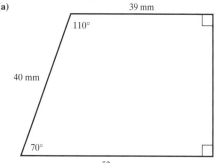

(b)

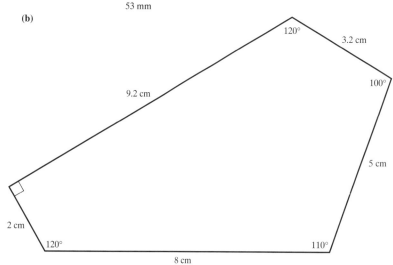

2 The trapezium on the RHS does not 'meet' the sides of the 2 triangles and the rectangle, to close up to make the 5th side.
3 (b)

(b) $c = 36°$ (vertically opposite angles, base angles of an isosceles triangle, alternate angles)
$d = 36°$ (corresponding angles, vertically opposite angles)
$e = 108°$ (vertically opposite angles, base angles of isosceles triangle and angles of a triangle add up to 180°; vertically opposite angles)
(c) $f = 38°$ (angles of a triangle add up to 180°)
$g = 76°$ (alternate angles, base angles of an isosceles triangle and angles of a triangle add up to 180°)
$h = 38°$
5 40; 6840°
6 (a) $a = 100°$
(b) $x = 130°$
(c) $b = 225°$

4 (a) $a = 41°$ (vertically opposite angles, corresponding angles, base angles of an isosceles triangle, angles of a triangle add up to 180°)
$b = 93°$ (exterior angle of a triangle)

Exercise 9F

1 (a) 050° (b) 056° (c) 232°
   (d) 247° (e) 289° (f) 286°
   (g) 232° (h) 180°

2

3 130°
4 235°
5 (a) 024°
   (b) 072°
   (c) 204°
   (d) 317°

Exercise 10A

1 Give different meal options that are served in the canteen. Ask for the frequency that the different meal options are chosen. Give several different options that students may want to have served in the canteen that are not already served.

2

Drinks	Tally	Frequency
Coffee	‖‖‖ ‖‖‖	10
Coke	‖‖‖ ‖‖	7
Lemon	‖‖‖‖	4
Tea	‖‖‖ ‖‖	7
Orange	‖‖‖	3
Milk	‖	1
	TOTAL	32

3 She could add up her 9 marks and divide by 9 to give the average for the 9 Science homeworks.

4

Meal options	Tally	Frequency

5

Age	Tally	Frequency
$0 < a \leqslant 5$		0
$5 < a \leqslant 10$	‖‖‖‖	4
$10 < a \leqslant 15$	‖‖‖ ‖‖	7
$15 < a \leqslant 20$	‖‖‖ ‖‖‖ ‖	11
$20 < a \leqslant 25$	‖‖‖ ‖	6
$25 < a \leqslant 30$	‖‖‖ ‖‖	7
$30 < a \leqslant 35$	‖‖‖	3
$35 < a \leqslant 40$	‖‖‖	3
$40 < a \leqslant 45$	‖‖‖ ‖‖‖	8
$45 < a \leqslant 50$		0
$50 < a \leqslant 55$	‖‖‖‖	4
$55 < a \leqslant 60$	‖‖	2
$60 < a \leqslant 65$	‖‖	2
$65 < a \leqslant 70$	‖‖	2
$70 < a \leqslant 75$	‖	1
	TOTAL	60

6

	Videos	DVDs	Totals
Boys	21	**17**	38
Girls	**15**	27	**42**
Totals	**36**	**44**	80

Exercise 11A

1 (a) $\frac{4}{12} = \frac{1}{3}$ (b) $\frac{9}{12} = \frac{3}{4}$
   (c) 0   (d) $\frac{7}{12}$
2 $\frac{997}{1000}$
3 0.998
4 4%
5 (a) 0.2   (b) 0.48   (c) 0.55
6 0.21
7 They are not mutually exclusive events.

Exercise 11B

1 (win, win) (win, lose) (win, draw)
   (lose, win) (lose, lose) (lose, draw)
   (draw, win) (draw, lose) (draw, draw)
2 (a) (Red, 1) (Red, 2) (Red, 3) (Red, 4)
      (Red, 5)
      (White, 1) (White, 2) (White, 3)
      (White, 4) (White, 5)
      (Blue, 1) (Blue, 2) (Blue, 3)
      (Blue, 4) (Blue, 5)
   (b) $\frac{1}{15}$
3 Leeds by car
   Leeds by bus
   Leeds by train

   York by car
   York by bus
   York by train

   Hull by car
   Hull by bus
   Hull by train

   Sheffield by car
   Sheffield by bus
   Sheffield by train

   Bolton by car
   Bolton by bus
   Bolton by train

4 (a) (A, 1) (A, 2) (A, 3) (A, 4) (A, 5)
      (A, 6)
      (B, 1) (B, 2) (B, 3) (B, 4) (B, 5)
      (B, 6)
      (C, 1) (C, 2) (C, 3) (C, 4) (C, 5)
      (C, 6)
      (D, 1) (D, 2) (D, 3) (D, 4) (D, 5)
      (D, 6)
      (E, 1) (E, 2) (E, 3) (E, 4) (E, 5)
      (E, 6)
   (b) $\frac{1}{30}$

5

		2nd spin		
		1	2	3
1st spin	1	2	3	4
	2	3	4	5
	3	4	5	6

Examination style practice paper

Section 1
1 (a) 29, 31
   (b) 36
2 (a)

		Second match		
		W	D	L
First match	W	6	4	3
	D	4	2	1
	L	3	1	0

   (b) $3x + y$
3 (a) $1\frac{5}{12}$ (b) $1\frac{13}{15}$

4 **(a)** Reflect in y-axis

(b)

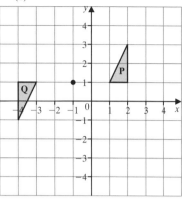

5 **(a)** $4n + 2$

(b) 12

Section 2

1 **(a)** $2p - 5q$

(b) $21cd$

(c) $y(y + 5)$

2

Age (years)	Favourite channel				
	BBC1	BBC2	ITV	Channel 4	Channel 5
$10 \leqslant a < 11$					
$11 \leqslant a < 12$					
$\vdots$					
$18 \leqslant a < 19$					

3 **(a)** $x = 45$ **(b)** $y = 44$

4 68%

5 058°

6 $x = -3$